# SPACE AGE CHRISTIANITY

# SPACE AGE CHRISTIANITY

*Edited by*

THE RT. REV. STEPHEN F. BAYNE, JR.
*Anglican Executive Officer*

*Foreword by*

The Rt. Rev. William Fisher Lewis
*Bishop of Olympia*

MOREHOUSE-BARLOW CO.

NEW YORK

PRINTED IN THE UNITED STATES OF AMERICA
BY THE HADDON CRAFTSMEN, INC., SCRANTON, PA.

# *Foreword*

## The Bishop of Olympia

Y E SHALL know the truth, and the truth shall make
you free"; so the Fourth Gospel quotes our Lord, and
it might serve as a text for this volume. *Not* that you, hope-
ful reader, will find in its pages a neat draught of truth, nor
a clear statement of *the truth as this Church has received
the same,* which you can accept as shield and refuge in
a time of confusion and doubt. Not that you will even
find the learned speakers coming to harmonious unity
after solemn discussion, for if you are looking for any
such assurance of reconciliation between science and religion, a simple "happy-pill" of ultimate agreement, this
is the wrong prescription altogether. The infinite God and
His creation are far too great for such comforts for our
intellects.

From the beginning of this venture, however, all
involved were and are, I think, united by the conviction
that *Truth is to be known.* The proper use of the minds
of men is the most searching inquiry into everything
visible and invisible that can be known to us. Surely the
Church has been least loyal to the Lord who is the Truth,
when she undertook to protect Him from those who would
know more of His work and His purpose. Surely the

answer to our uncertainty in the face of our world and our future in it is more knowledge and not less. The Christian says that God revealed Himself to men and surely the search for further knowledge is the only proper expression of our gratitude and our conviction.

Truth can be, must be, known. And that Reality whom the Christian calls God wills our knowledge and lays on us the obligation to seek further for all truth. I am delighted to have been a bystander in this undertaking of our Laity in which they raised the curtain for four evenings on some of the complexities of this search. To those responsible I have already said a personal thanks. To our very distinguished speakers who shared their convictions and experience, that we might see something of the immensity of the problems involved, we all owe more than we can repay. I commend this book to all of you who may be in any way interested in the place of Christianity in the intellectual life of our time; and who would be sure that Religion and Truth are inseparable in spite of all the limitations of our knowledge.

Finally I would add my thanks to all who had a part in this program. Their names are listed in the Publisher's Preface, but our most special thanks go to Bishop Bayne for his encouragement in the early stages, for his advice and wisdom in many of our plans, for his part in the program itself, and finally for his editorship of this book. May all our efforts be useful to God and His Kingdom.

WM. FISHER LEWIS
*Bishop of Olympia*

# Publisher's Preface

THIS book is an edited account of the lectures and discussions on *Space Age Christianity* which took place in August 1962 at the Seattle World's Fair.

## THE PARTICIPANTS

### I. *The Physical Sciences*

The Rev. William G. Pollard was the first speaker, not only on this topic but also in the symposium. He is Executive Director of the Oak Ridge Institute of Nuclear Studies, and priest-associate of St. Stephen's Church, Oak Ridge, Tennessee. Dr. Pollard did his graduate work in physics at Rice Institute. After a time as a teacher, he was swept into the "Manhattan Project" (code name for the first atomic bomb program), and spent two years in the final stages of development of that weapon. Following the war he went almost at once to Oak Ridge, where he has been in charge, since 1947, of the immensely significant work of that Institute, now the principal American agency in the exploration of the "peaceful uses" of the atom. In 1954, Dr. Pollard was ordained to the priesthood, beginning a double ministry such as few men are privileged to have. This was his second visit to the diocese of Olympia.

He shared, in 1957, a symposium on the Christian Doctrine of Work, in connection with the tenth anniversary of Bishop Bayne's consecration.

Edward C. Wells was the second speaker on the Physical Sciences. A Seattlite, he is a vice-president and director of the Boeing Aircraft Co., and in charge of its Military Aircraft Systems Division. Following graduation from Stanford University, he became identified with the aircraft industry in which he has served ever since. He shared in the design and development of the famous Boeing bombers—the B-17 and the B-29—as well as the 707 Stratotanker, the forerunner of the notable 707 passenger airplane. His present responsibility is primarily to direct the design, development, and production of military aircraft weapons systems, a most sensitive and central responsibility in national life, and one which keeps him constantly on the frontier of scientific and technical developments. Yet as a Churchman and citizen, he is of necessity obliged to look at all he deals with from the vantage point of both the Christian faith and responsible, democratic citizenship. He is a Fellow and sometime President of the Institute of Aeronautical Sciences, a member of the Society of Automotive Engineers, and a recipient of the Lawrence Sperry Award.

## II. *The Biological Sciences*

Dr. Paul Dudley White was the first speaker in this field. Among the most distinguished of American physicians, he came into international prominence as the personal physician to President Eisenhower, notably at the time of the President's coronary attack. A graduate of

Harvard in 1908, he also took his medical degree there, and in 1950 was made a Doctor of Science, *honoris causa*, of the same university. His honors are very great and deservedly so—Greece, Czechoslovakia, Cuba, and France have all paid him signal tribute, as well as his own native country, where he received the Lasker Award for distinguished achievement in the field of cardiovascular diseases. He is a member of societies of cardiac specialists in France, Mexico, Brazil, Chile, Australia, and South Africa, an authoritative writer—particularly in his special field of cardiac illness—and a tireless lecturer and commentator.

Dr. Franklin K. Murphy, Chancellor of the University of California in Los Angeles, is also a physician, who has devoted much of his life to academic leadership. After graduation from the University of Kansas and the School of Medicine of the University of Pennsylvania, he devoted the years of his military service to research in tropical diseases. From 1951 to 1960 he was Chancellor of the University of Kansas. In 1958, he was one of seven American university presidents to visit Russian universities and technical institutes as an official delegate under the U.S.A.-U.S.S.R. agreement for the exchange of persons in the scientific and cultural fields. His interests are most wide—apart from technical medical societies, he is also a member of such diverse groups as the Kress and Menninger Foundations, the National Council of the Boy Scouts of America, and the special committee on the University and World Affairs of the Ford Foundation.

### III. *The Social Sciences*

J. Milton Yinger, the first speaker on the Social Sciences, is one of America's foremost sociologists, now professor of sociology and anthropology at Oberlin College. Previously he held the same chair at Ohio Weselyan University, and has also held visiting professorships in sociology at the Universities of Hawaii, Michigan, and Washington. He has been particularly interested in the sociology of religion. In 1962 he held a lectureship in the Paul H. Douglas Memorial of the Religious Research Association. His publications include *Religion in the Struggle for Power* (1946), *Racial and Cultural Minorities* (1953-8) and *Religion, Society and the Individual* (1957). He is Associate Editor, as well, of the American Sociological Review.

The Rev. Albert T. Mollegen, also speaking on the Social Sciences, is another old friend of the Diocese of Olympia, having been the leader of a special conference of the independent schools of the Pacific Northwest held in celebration of the 75th anniversary of the Annie Wright Seminary, the diocese's distinguished school for girls. As well, he was a teacher of a number of the diocesan clergy, having been on the faculty of the Virginia Theological Seminary since 1944. A graduate of Virginia, he did his postgraduate study at Union Theological Seminary. He occupies one of the broadest chairs in American life as Professor of Christian Ethics and New Testament Language and Literature. Apart from his formal teaching responsibilities, he has interested himself particularly in the social sciences—notably in the field of pastoral psychology—and is one of the Church's pioneer leaders on that frontier.

## IV. *Worship, Unity, Stewardship*

The Rt. Rev. Stephen F. Bayne, Jr., was the preacher at the closing session of the series (under the title quoted above), and was also the Moderator of the three evenings of discussion. Bishop Bayne is presently the Anglican Executive Officer, the principal minister of liaison and coordination among the eighteen churches of the Anglican Communion. From 1947 to 1960 he was Bishop of the Diocese of Olympia, coming to that post from Columbia University, where he had been the Chaplain. A New Yorker, he was born in 1908, educated at Trinity School, New York, Amherst College and the General Theological Seminary. After serving as Fellow and Tutor of the General Seminary, he ministered in parishes in St. Louis, Missouri, and Northampton, Mass., before going to Columbia in 1942. From 1944 to 1946 he was a chaplain in the U.S.N.R. on leave from Columbia.

Bishop Bayne, beside participating in the program, edited this volume and contributed the introduction and summary.

## THE "REACTORS"

In addition to the seven speakers here identified, nine members of the Diocese of Olympia—lay and clerical—also shared in the programs as "Reactors." They are:

*First session*—the Rev. Wesley Frensdorff, dean-elect of the Cathedral in Salt Lake City; Miss Ruth Jenkins, headmistress of the Annie Wright Seminary, girls' school of the Diocese of Olympia; Mr. Daniel Luzon Morris, a mathematician and teacher of science at Lakeside School, Seattle, and author of *Possibilities Unlimited*, (Harper & Row, New York).

*Second session*—Mrs. Howard M. Heckedorn, wife of a Seattle physician, and herself an active worker in Christian Education; Dr. Robert Barnes, physician and chief of staff of Doctor's Hospital, Seattle; the Rev. Matthew Bigliardi, rector, Emmanuel Church, Mercer Island.

*Third session*—Mr. William Adams II, executive vice president of the Seattle Chamber of Commerce; Miss Louise Bowler, executive director of Faith House, Tacoma (a diocesan agency for unwed mothers), and graduate social case-worker; the Rev. Paul Langpaap, rector, Trinity Church, Seattle.

## Other Participants

Finally, "participants" should include a host of others, not only those who attended but also those who had a hand in planning and presenting the symposium. They are as follows:

### Arrangements by the Diocese of Olympia, Seattle, Washington

*Co-Chairmen of the Department of the Laity*

* Mrs. B. Franklin Miller
* Myron C. Calkins

*Co-Chairmen of the Space Age Christianity Program*

\* L. Donald Bridenbaugh, M.D.
\* B. Franklin Miller

\* Members of the Department of the Laity

*Planning Committee*

The Rev. Matthew Bigliardi, Rector, Emmanuel Church, Mercer Island

Thomas Carlile, M.D.—Radiologist; Pres. American Cancer Society

Edward E. Carlson; President Western Hotels; Chairman Washington State World's Fair Commission

The Rev. Elmer B. Christie, Rector, Church of the Epiphany, Seattle

* The Rev. Canon Rudolf Devik, Asst. to the Bishop, Diocese of Olympia

C. Clement French, President, Washington State University

Gordon W. Ingham, retired

Wylie Hemphill, property management

Robert L. King, M.D.—Cardiologist; past president American Heart Assn.

The Very Rev. John Leffler, Dean, St. Mark's Cathedral, Seattle

* The Rt. Rev. Wm. F. Lewis, Bishop, Diocese of Olympia

Richard Maginot, Sales Promotion Manager, Bon Marche

Joseph McCarthy, Dean, Graduate School & Director of Office of University Research, University of Washington

Brig. Gen. William A. Millington, USMC Ret., Acacia Cemetery

Harold Shefelman, Lawyer, Weter Roberts and Shefelman, past president Municipal League

* Members of the Department of the Laity

George Stoner, Vice President, Boeing Company;
Director Dyna-Soar Project

The Rev. Carl Tamblyn, Rector, St. Stephen's Church,
Laurelhurst, Seattle

* The Rev. Canon Richard Williams, director Stewardship, Diocese of Olympia

### Administrative Committee

* The Rev. Kenneth Allen, Jr.
  The Rev. Robert L. Baxter, Jr.
* Mr. and Mrs. Ernest L. Belknap
* Mrs. Myron Calkins
* George Farnsworth
* The Rev. Wesley Frensdorff
  Peter Hallock
* Andrew Hess
* Mr. and Mrs. Robert P. Hutchinson
* Mrs. Warner A. Paul
* Lionel Schmidt
  W. Paul Uhlmann
* The Rev. John Barry Winn

* Members of the Department of the Laity

# Contents

FOREWORD, by the Bishop of Olympia ..............   5

PUBLISHER'S PREFACE
    The Participants .................................   7
    The "Reactors" .................................  11
    Arrangements by the Diocese of Olympia ...........  12

INTRODUCTION
    *The Rt. Rev. Stephen F. Bayne, Jr.* .............  17

  I. THE PHYSICAL SCIENCES
    Christianity in the Space Age
        *The Rev. William G. Pollard* ..................  25
    Self-Critical Questions
        *Edward C. Wells* ............................  39
    Discussion One ..................................  44

 II. THE BIOLOGICAL SCIENCES
    The Biological Sciences
        *Dr. Paul Dudley White* ......................  61
    Faith and Reason in an Age of Discovery
        *Dr. Franklin D. Murphy* ......................  78
    Discussion Two .................................  88

III. THE SOCIAL SCIENCES
    The Social Sciences in the Space Age
        *Prof. J. Milton Yinger* ........................  111

The Christian Ethos of Empirical Science
   *The Rev. A. T. Mollegen* ...................... 138
Discussion Three ............................... 149

IV.  WORSHIP, UNITY, AND STEWARDSHIP
   A Sermon
   *The Rt. Rev. Stephen F. Bayne, Jr.* .............. 165

SUMMARY
   *The Rt. Rev. Stephen F. Bayne, Jr.* .............. 181

BIBLIOGRAPHY .................................... 189

# Introduction

FIRST, let me say something about the background of the symposium. It was first imagined by some of the Diocese of Olympia's lay deputies and visitors at the General Convention in Detroit, in September 1961. In conversation, several of them expressed their disquiet that at the forthcoming Seattle World's Fair—"Century 21"— there was apparently to be no program or exhibit focussing on the theological implications of the scientific and technological developments which were inescapably the heart of the Fair, as they are of our times. There were religious exhibits of various kinds at the Fair, notably that of the Seattle Council of Churches in which the Diocese of Olympia took its part. But the most important issue— that of the questions which Christian faith and scientific development posed to each other—seemed not to be included. Ought not the Church do what it could to redress this imbalance? Could the Church not at least bring together a group of Churchmen scientists, and theologians, able to think and speak freely about these implications, to engage in a witnessing and enquiring dialogue?

The Bishop of Olympia was immediately warm in his support of the suggestion, as was I, once their bishop and still an affectionate comrade. The proposal was promptly discussed by the diocesan Department of the Laity, and the Diocesan Council, and was adopted; and within a few months the design of the symposium was complete and the participants chosen. Throughout the Spring and early Summer of 1962, the Department of the Laity, with the help of scores of other lay people of the diocese, were hard at work. Arrangements were made with the World's Fair to set aside four evenings for the meetings. The new Playhouse was engaged for the three nights of discussion, and the Opera House secured for the service of thanksgiving and witness which closed the program. Arrangements were made with local radio and television stations to provide full coverage. Four half-hour television recordings were planned (in which the principal speakers all shared in turn) in joint co-operation with KING-TV in Seattle and the Episcopal Church's Division of Radio and Television. Innumerable plans had to be made for the working details of the four evenings. The not-inconsiderable funds required were raised by a great number of gifts from members of the diocese as well as from the advance sale of tickets. Arrangements were happily made for the editing and publication of this volume.

I mention all these matters chiefly to stress what seems to me still the remarkable and buoyant leadership of the laity of a diocese, who felt a responsible concern to act for the faith in a critically-important sector of life. Their intention and understanding were well expressed in the statement printed on the programs:

> The Department of the Laity of the Diocese of Olympia presents this program and offers it to the greater Glory of God.
>
> As this Department has worked to understand afresh the function of the Laity in the Church, they have seen increasingly that God is served and worshipped within the world in

which we live, and not merely beside it. This world of work, of increasing knowledge, and of community responsibility and action is the world where God intends us, the Church, to be His agents and servants.

This Century 21 program is therefore offered to all who would serve Him now and in the century to come.

I should not want to seem neglectful of what the clergy did, in all this. As always, their help was needed and gladly sought and given. But I know that they felt, as I did, the significance as well as the joy of an adventure of this kind, imagined and fulfilled primarily by the responsible leadership of the laity.

Second, let me introduce the program itself. Its basic structure was very simple. In all the sparkling variety of the World's Fair, four evenings were set aside for it. On the first three evenings, the Playhouse (a new, small theatre seating some eight hundred) was used. Each evening there were two principal speakers—the first asked to present a major statement on the theme of the evening, the second to speak somewhat more briefly, addressing himself mainly to the statement and position of his predecessor. The other members of the symposium were also present, on the stage, each night; and at the conclusion of the two addresses they were invited to comment or question, or enter into dialogue with one another freely, as long as they wished.

Following this, three "reactors" were asked to comment or raise questions, directing their remarks to either of the speakers or to the whole panel. These "reactors" were simply representative men and women (including one clergyman each evening) whose function it was to serve as surrogates for the eight hundred in the audience. Any general discussion or questioning seemed impossible, because

of the size of the group. Therefore the three representatives were asked to think of themselves as the minds and
consciences of the whole *laos* assembled, and to try to
speak as their deputies.

Finally I, as the Moderator, attempted a very brief
summary of each evening. This turned out to be little more
than fragments of the speech I would have made that evening if allowed. I have included these summaries in the text
following, but not in any pride of authorship, nor indeed
for any other purpose than to indicate something of the
point I felt we had reached at the end of each two-hour
session. Then the Bishop let us depart with a blessing.

The final evening was necessarily of a different character. All those concerned in planning the program felt that
it should end with worship, and with an attempt on my
part to correlate the life of Christian faith with all that had
been said about three very diverse fields of knowledge the
preceding evenings. For this purpose, the assembly moved
to the Opera House seating some 3,500. Evening Prayer
was sung and my address was in fact a sermon. Like most
sermons, there wasn't any chance for anybody to argue
back. Such dialogue as there was had to be unspoken, and
desired and sought by the preacher (which was the case);
but in any event, the fourth section of the text following
contains only the words of the sermon, I'm afraid.

Third, let me say something about this book. I am myself most grateful to Morehouse-Barlow for their interest
in publishing this summary and record of four evenings
of dialogue in the Church, covering an area of the most
critical importance and sensitivity for Christian witness.
They have asked me to edit it, and I am glad to do so. The
only difficult part of the editor's duty has been to pluck

out the plums from the pudding of discussion each of the first three evenings. It would have been easier simply to print the whole transcript; but space did not permit. So I have tried to preserve the core of each evening's conversation, including some of the brilliant asides, wise saws, and improved second thoughts of my distinguished colleagues, but not all.

Briefly, the plan of the book is simply that of printing, first of all, the two addresses on each of the three topics, and then following immediately, in the same section, with excerpts from the taped discussion. Thus there are three main sections corresponding with the three topics and the three evenings of discussion. Then my closing sermon composes the fourth main section. At the end, I have attempted a very brief summary and critique. My own editorial comments in the four main sections of the book are limited simply to those I felt necessary to present the material fairly.

STEPHEN F. BAYNE, JR.

# I

# THE PHYSICAL SCIENCES

THE REV. WILLIAM G. POLLARD
EDWARD C. WELLS

*Discussion "Reactors":*

The Rev. Wesley Frensdorff
Miss Ruth Jenkins
Daniel Luzon Morris

# Christianity in the Space Age

The Rev. William G. Pollard

IN CHOOSING the name "Century 21" for the Seattle World's Fair, those who planned it gave expression to the enthusiasm for science which characterizes our age and to the confident expectation of all that ever bigger and better things are to come from it right on through the next century. There is no question of the rightness of their choice. Its appropriateness in reflecting a universal passion and hope of the mid-twentieth century is attested by the favorable response which the name receives from all who know the Fair.

Many dark and terrible things surround the mid-twentieth century, but its glory for both free world and communist alike is in its science and technology. We are living in the midst of a Golden Age, and it is natural that we should expect such an age to continue indefinitely and to advance continually to ever greater and greater achievements. The people who have lived in the midst of the various golden ages of the past have had the same hopes about their own time.

My own expectations for the twenty-first century are rather different from this. To me it seems much more probable that something quite new and different and unexpected will gradually emerge as Century 21 unfolds. The people of that century will slowly come to recognize that new thing as the dominant characteristic of their age, in the same way that we all now recognize science and technology as the uniquely governing spirit of our time. This is not to say that there will not be science and technology on a greatly expanded scale in Century 21. That is guaranteed by the world wide explosion of human population and the "revolution of rising expectations" for the better things of the scientific age which is now in full swing among long dormant and underdeveloped peoples. Only a greatly expanded science and technology can possibly support throughout the twenty-first century the world wide population and civilization which is now in the making.

My point is rather that science and technology will by then simply have become the accepted taken-for-granted elements of our common life. They will no longer constitute the dominant enthusiasm and passion of the people. Instead they will look back on the twentieth century as the age when the great breakthroughs and achievements were made in science and technology, just as we now look back on the fifteenth century as the age of enormously expanded geographical horizons—the age of adventure and discovery in opening up the whole round earth to man's knowledge and dominion.

In saying this I would not for a moment want you to think that I am critical of the golden age of science as being somehow unworthy, or that I am dissociating myself from a full sharing in the dominant passions and enthusiasms of this age. I have had the unique experience of starting out in physics in the late twenties and of being a full participant in the enormously exciting and spectacular march of science during the past thirty years. I love physics and glory in the wonders of its intellectual and practical achievements. I thank God daily for the unique privilege of having been born at such a critical moment, and of having been endowed with sufficient gifts to be an active participant in such a glorious adventure of the human spirit. More than most people, I have a deep respect for and appreciation of the inner beauty and majesty of modern theoretical physics, the astounding maturity of understanding of nature which modern science has given man, and the extraordinary mastery and control over the processes of nature which modern science has provided man as a fruit of this understanding. The material evidences of big science in our day—the monolithic nuclear reactors, the intricately precise mile long particle accelerators, the mighty rockets and space ships, and the great sprawling research laboratories of the Atomic Energy Commission and the National Aeronautics and Space Administration— are all outward and visible signs of an inward and spiritual dynamism and power unsurpassed in all human history. I share fully in the passionate involvement in and enthusiasm for science which characterizes our age. I would not have missed it for anything. In the unfolding providence of Almighty God, it is truly wonderful to behold what great things are being accomplished in our time, and it is a choice role to have been given to have been made an active participant in scientific achievement.

But having said this, it is also necessary to add a few words of caution by way of balance. I suppose that it is an inevitable property of the people who live in any golden age to be so passionately devoted to the spirit of their age that all other aspects of reality extraneous to it are excluded. Because of this, perhaps, it is easy to be misunderstood when I speak of the limitations and shortcoming of science, as well as emphasizing its glories. Yet science does have its limitations, and when these are not recognized or admitted the very passion for science which characterizes our age is its gravest danger.

I am convinced there are ways in which our great admiration for science, and our dogmatic exclusion of all non-scientific aspects of reality have become a secret snare and delusion for us. Subtly and without our realization of what was happening to us, this exclusive passion for one very fruitful access to reality has been slowly excluding us from other older routes which used to provide the framework within which man's life was lived and nourished with power from on high. It is this dogmatic rejection of all which lies outside the domain of science that constitutes its peril. Just because an entire culture, or even a whole age like our own, loses the capacity to respond to any but one aspect of reality does not change the structure of reality itself. That which is and exists does not cease to be simply because people cease to believe in it.

Two inherent dangers in science exist, both of which have been largely realized in this century of its cultural fruition and triumph. The first of these arises out of the inherent limitation imposed on science by the fact that it is restricted to the study of nature. The other arises out of its necessary confinement to those aspects of nature which are regular, coherent, and repeatable at will. The more our knowledge of the natural has grown, the more we have lost our former capacity to respond to supernatural reality transcendent to nature. The more we have discovered of the lawful and dependable undergirding of events, the more the capacity we formerly had to discern the divine hand in the great turning points of life and history has faded. Yet these decisive events are essentially indeterminate and singular, and so beyond the reach of science to make lawful and predictable. As a result the rise of science has brought with it an ever increasing imprisonment of the mind and spirit of man in space, time, and matter.

It is this imprisonment of the spirit of man, this total bondage to the here and now, which seems to me to set the stage for the next great development. The twentieth century, for all the glory of its scientific achievement, is a kind of dark age. The renaissance or rediscovery of lost capacities of response to transcendent reality which alone will liberate the spirit of man from this bondage may well prove to be the distinguishing work of the twenty-first century. At least, while we are all trying our hand at gazing in the crystal ball, such possibility has as much to recommend it as those depicted at scientific exhibits, or prophesied from time to time in the daily press.

Toward the end of the last century a mathematical romance was published in England under the title *Flatland*. Written by the mathematician Edwin Abbott, it is the story of one Mr. A. Square who inhabited a two dimensional world of infinite extent. All objects and persons in Flatland had only length and breadth but no thickness. Yet the Flatlanders themselves, apart from A. Square, were not conscious of this as a limitation. It seemed reasonable and obvious to them that everything which existed should be contained within their two-dimensional domain. They could not even imagine a direction along which a perpendicular to Flatland would lie. The central part of the story concerns a visit to A. Square from a spacelander, a sphere, who suddenly appeared in his living room one evening as a circle of varying size. All that was visible of him was his intersection with Flatland, and that is of course a circle. Yet the circle miraculously appeared and disappeared in A. Square's living room. All the sphere had to do to make this happen was to exercise his three-dimensional capacity to move toward or away from Flatland along a perpendicular to it.

A very interesting conversation ensues between the square and the circle. At the end of it, A. Square, assisted by the sphere, is jerked with a traumatic effort right out of Flatland into the surrounding space. In his amazing journey he is able to perceive the whole of his Flatland domain spread out before him. He sees, moreover, the insides of things. Houses and rooms and people are completely open to his inspection and examination. It becomes clear to him, as it could never have been before, that his entire natural world of two dimensions is simply immersed in space. Every point of Flatland was in immediate contact with the far wider and freer realities of space. To be born into Flatland was to enter upon a mode of existence severely limited by comparison with the wider freedom and potentiality of spatial existence. Yet every object in Flatland was nevertheless always in immediate contact with this transcendent domain, for wherever one went it was always right there perpendicular to him. When A. Square returned from this journey, he was bursting with his desire to make these aspects clear to his fellow Flatlanders. They, however, scorned such strange notions and ended up by locking him up for the rest of his life.

The significance of this romance is that it suggests how the whole space-time universe within which we have entered upon our existence is similarly limited and similarly immersed in a larger reality. Yet for most of his life on this planet man has always thought of this earthly mode of existence as one immersed in a higher transcendent reality which was everywhere and always in immediate contact with him. The natural was immersed in the supernatural, and the temporal in the eternal. In opening up the vast reaches of space and equally vast spans of time to our apprehension, science has seemed to banish the supernatural and the transcendent. One can imagine a similar age in the history of Flatland, a golden age of science and discovery when Flatlander astronomers showed that Flatland extended in every direction for billions of light years. In such an age a Flatland Khrushchev or Titov might even announce that there was no heaven, or paradise, or angels because they had made a trip in a two-dimensional rocket and had not been able to find them anywhere in Flatland. The more remarkable and wonderful the discoveries made by Flatlander scientists in such an age, the more unnecessarily tragic would be the complete imprisonment within their own two-dimensional domain to which they would condemn their contemporaries.

Just such a tragedy is the complete imprisonment of modern man within our domain of space, time, and matter. We should *know* that the whole space-time continuum is immersed in a higher reality transcendent to it. We should *know* this from the whole weight of the accumulated experience and witness of the race. Think of what men have known in former ages of the power and reality of spirit, of the awesome experience of the holy, and of the awareness of the divine presence. Consider in the light of the analogy with Flatland the meaning of these verses from the 139th Psalm:

Whither shall I go then from thy Spirit? or whither shall I go then from thy presence?

If I climb up into heaven thou art there; if I go down to hell, thou art there also.

If I take the wings of the morning, and remain in the uttermost  parts of the sea;

Even there also shall thy hand lead me, and thy right hand shall hold me.

Colonel John H. Glenn, Jr., expressed this same thought after his rocket trip. It is clear that however far we may venture into space, our relationship to the transcendent realities in which we are all immersed will be exactly the same as it is here. In order to really reach heaven, Mr. Khrushchev and his scientists would have to learn how to shoot rockets perpendicular to the whole space-time continuum, right out of our domain of existence. But there is no way in which science can learn or teach us how to do that. In order to learn something of heaven and eternity and of the relation in which nature stands to supernature, one has to turn from the scientific heritage to the great religious heritage of the West. And that is precisely what twentieth-century man is unable to do any more.

There are many evidences of the extent to which twentieth-century culture has built barriers which effectively shield us from any apprehension of transcendental reality. One of these is the character of education. It is instructive to examine the content and implied or unexpressed assumptions of both secondary school and college courses, not only in the sciences but in philosophy, history, and literature as well. The spirit which pervades all of them is the demand that all proper knowledge and admissable explanation be in terms of objects and events within space and time. The supernatural and the transcendent are every-where regarded as mere inner subjective states with no ex-ternal reference in reality. It is often pointed out that science has "liberated" man from age old superstitions and fears, from supposedly false interpretations of phenomena in terms of gods and demons.

There is just enough truth in such an attitude to make each new generation educated in this manner that much less aware of the extent to which they are being made im-mune to any effective response to reality beyond space and time. No scientific basis whatever exists for the universal assumption that the explanation for everything which is and happens in space and time must be found within space and time. Yet the sheer unanimity of agreement on this axiom of the entire educational process gives it an unas-sailable dogmatic force. In liberating man from false super-stitions, science has unwittingly locked him securely in an-other prison of its own making. This prison is the exclusive bondage to nature and the natural. Modern man cannot even conceive any longer of any possible way of escape from nature. He cannot imagine any place transcendent to nature where he might go if he were to leave it. In many ways this bondage is worse than the ancient bondages from which science has liberated man.

Another way to see this point is to consider what the twentieth century has done to the arts. As far back as we have any record of human culture at all, art and poetry have been the means by which men have communicated with each other their experience of supernatural and tran-scendent reality. The arts are the vehicle by means of which men communicate the inexpressible and share a common experience of the reality of things invisible and unseen. In any previous age when supernatural reality was as much a common property and heritage of the whole of culture as the world of nature, they had a public function as important as that of the expository and logical use of language and mathematics by which men share their knowledge of the visible, natural world.

But in this age which has lost all effective contact with transcendent reality, there is nothing external to man left to communicate. This is the real trouble with art and poetry today. Our artists, poets, and musicians are just as able, sensitive, and skillful as those of past centuries. The trouble is not with them but with us. For the world in which they live forces them to speak into a vacuum. The only things left for art and poetry and music to express are the inner subjective states and feelings of the artist. Insofar as others are able to share in these same inner subjective states and feelings, the artist communicates and his work is considered successful. But it is a very different thing to be an artist in an age for which the only realities other than space, time, and matter are subjective feelings generated by the complexities of the human nervous system. What a contrast to artists in the past who could do their work in an age for which the supernatural world was as real as the natural and for which the overarching majesty and living power of the divine transcendent was an integral part of the common experience of all. Any treatise or course on the theory of art or on art appreciation today provides substantial evidence that the vanishing of this world is the root cause of the sickness of the arts in this century.

Another way in which the bondage of our age to the here and now is especially manifest appears in its attitude toward death. Someone has said that just as the unmentionable topic for the Victorian nineteenth century was sex, so the unmentionable topic for the golden age of science in the twentieth century is death. It is easy to see why it should be. For if there is no way to escape from space, time, and matter, if nothing exists outside of, or transcendent to, nature, then there is no longer any mystery about death. What happens to those who die in such an exclusively natural world is quite clear and easily verified. Modern man knows this in his heart, and it is here that the prison within which his culture has so securely bound him becomes most poignantly terrible and unbearable for him. Small wonder that he cannot bring himself to mention or even think about the subject of death! The past three centuries during which science has made its spectacular achievements in our understanding and control of nature, have at the same time herded the whole of mankind into a spiritual prison in which all men in this century again "sit in darkness, and in the shadow of death."

Yet the transcendent reality in which the space-time continuum is immersed remains just as real as it ever was. It is not affected in any way by the loss of the capacity of twentieth-century man to apprehend it and respond to it. The answer to death has been given concretely in the real history of this earth through the empty tomb and the resurrected Christ. That astounding event, of such ultimate significance and import, is just as true as it ever was. The fact of it is in no way affected by the twentieth century's widespread disbelief in it.

Yet the significance of this supernatural event lies precisely in making manifest to us the possibility of escaping from our bondage to space, time, and matter. For the Lord clearly rose from death into a very different state of being from that which he voluntarily assumed in the Incarnation, when the Word was made flesh and dwelt among us under the same limitations which we are under in this world. Just as the sphere was able to enter or leave Flatland at will, and appear to the Flatlanders as the circle which was all that could be seen of him within the limitations of a two-dimensional mode of existence, so the risen Christ could enter or leave our space-time domain at will, and appear or disappear to his disciples in the body which they had known and loved. And just as the sphere was able to assist the square in escaping from his confinement to Flatland into the wider freedom of space, so our Lord stands ready to raise all who believe in Him, just as He was raised, right out of space and time into the wider freedom of eternity and the transcendent domain within which space is immersed.

In an age which has lost all effective contact with the supernatural, and cannot even imagine any reality beyond space and time, the Resurrection naturally seems absurd and must be interpreted as a peculiar subjective hallucination of those who witnessed it. Yet it remains the most important fact of all history for man to know and respond to. It is just as true today as it was then that God intended it "to give light to them that sit in darkness, and in the shadow of death, and to guide our feet into the way of peace", as the *Benedictus* puts it.

I am persuaded that man is not doomed to remain indefinitely within this prison wrought by science. Even now one senses a great world-wide longing of the human spirit to escape from it. The pressure of this longing can only increase as the remainder of this century unfolds. I am convinced that a renaissance of discovery of supernatural reality has even now begun. Like every renaissance it will be a slow process of historic growth. One does not revolutionize patterns of thought and the pervasive convictions of a whole culture overnight. The very existence of this renaissance will remain undetectable to the vast majority of people for several decades more. It is necessarily so with every renaissance. Its origin and development can only be discerned in the retrospect of history after it has come to full flower.

For its contemporaries, it is always too small and inconspicuous to be seen or appreciated. Yet the chosen few who make up the early renaissance, men living in the prevailing dark age around them, do sense it and discern something of its power to finally transform the culture within which it has taken root. This is my own feeling about my ministry. I think of myself as a renaissance man in the vanguard of a growing world-wide movement of rediscovery. I do not think that I shall see its fruits, but I rejoice that God in the mystery of His grace should have touched me in the midstream of life and permitted me to see so clearly what still remains hidden from the majority of my contemporaries.

This then is what I see when I gaze into the crystal ball and try to discern what will be the dominant character of Century 21. There are still nearly four decades left in this century, and it will certainly take at least that long for what I discern to become generally detectable. But after that, as the twenty-first century unfolds, I feel confident that it will more and more be recognized as the century during which man regained his lost capacity to apprehend and respond to that reality all around him which is transcendent to space and time. At the same time it will be a century marked everywhere by science and technology. During the next four decades, the whole earth will certainly become fully industrialized, and science will bring forth innumerable new marvels scarcely imaginable now. But that will simply be the world in which twenty-first-century man finds himself. He will see his world as the great achievement of the twentieth century. For him the renaissance I have described, by then in full swing, will be the distinctive achievement which history and destiny holds out to him. And so Century 21 will not, I am convinced, see in science its distinctive mission as we in the twentieth century do. Rather for twenty-first-century man the ever widening horizons of the rediscovery of the richness and depth of supernatural reality will provide his challenge and his mission for achievement.

Since I know that I am an early renaissance man, I do not expect many of my contemporaries to share my vision, or to agree that what I discern has anything at all to do with what will really happen in the twenty-first century. We all see different things when we look into the crystal ball, and I am well aware that very few indeed see what I see. Moreover, I am also under an obligation to share with you something of my profound conviction that that which I discern is really the true key to Century 21, even though at this stage it remains hidden from most. Finally it must be evident to all of you by now how deeply I desire and long to share with you, and with everyone for whom God gives me the opportunity, the excitement and thrill of this venture for rediscovering that which so many in our day have lost and, even without knowing it, desire so desperately to have again.

# Self-Critical Questions

Edward C. Wells

IT IS INDEED a privilege to take part in this series on "Christianity in the Space Age," and in particular to follow Dr. Pollard, commenting upon his challenging address.

In my remarks I will not attempt to respond to Dr. Pollard point-by-point, as I believe the purpose of his paper may be better served by discussing his underlying theme, that of hope for and confidence in a return to awareness of the supernatural, and the advent of a new freedom from our dependence upon things of a material rather than spiritual nature.

Dr. Pollard has made each of us feel, as perhaps we had not felt before, an emotion of gratitude for the privilege of living in this age of scientific and material achievement. But he has at the same time reminded us forcefully that in our headlong progress in this one direction, we risk losing our way entirely. Truly we do live in a world of magnificent material and physical advancement. Just as truly however do we sometimes lack an awareness of what Dr. Pollard has termed the supernatural, that awareness so essential to a balanced existence, particularly in such a rapidly moving world.

For some, the scientific or material achievement serves

to quicken the pace toward the next assault on the material unknown, but for many, the purely material achievement will one day inevitably bring into focus our inability to be self sufficient—our need for spiritual as well as material growth. Dr. Pollard has given us new insight into this problem and renewed hope for a spiritual renaissance in Century 21, for an acceptance of the supernatural as exemplified by our Christian faith, for an unprecedented growth of human potential through spiritual nurture.

I fully accept and commend to you Dr. Polland's thesis of hope, his belief in the certainty of a new world of spiritual values in Century 21 which will transcend the greatest achievements of the present era. I trust that Dr. Pollard will permit me to differ with him on one matter, however, and that is the rate at which such a transformation might take place. Certainly there is evidence all around us of searching for a non-materialistic standard by which to measure human progress. That these papers are to be published for wider distribution is in itself evidence of a deep interest in spiritual values.

True, many of the daily events of our time could bring despair to the most optimistic mind. At the same time, however, we can be encouraged by signs on the positive side of the ledger. These signs give me hope that the renaissance can and may be well under way in Century 20, if we who otherwise might stand and wait for Century 21 and its great promise would instead extend ourselves to be effective in Century 20. The very magnitude of the progress toward scientific understanding in Century 20, the very wonders of the natural world which unfold before our eyes in scientific exhibits and elsewhere can only eventually focus increasing attention on those areas in which we are failing to make comparable advances.

Why, we may well ask, with such material progress must a spiritual awakening be further delayed? Why not, at least, a glimpse of a new horizon in Century 20, in our generation rather than the next? Dr. Pollard has capably presented the potential, and the ultimate certainty of this renaissance. What can be the stumbling blocks, if even a few early renaissance men and women believe passionately in the certainty of the new era as others have believed in the certainty of our present era?

What are the obstacles which we might effectively help to remove? Let me pose a few self-critical questions to illustrate:

Have we as professing Christians ever made a God of material wealth while professing to "have no other Gods before Thee"?

Have scientists, in pursuit of either scientific understanding or individual achievement ever overemphasized the scientific, the natural, the human achievement elements of our world to the exclusion of the extra-scientific and supernatural? If I may paraphrase Dr. Pollard's comment—"Is it not the dogmatic rejection of all which lies outside the domain of science that constitutes its greatest danger?"

Have men of religion, with their deep understanding of things spiritual and theological set up a God apart, a God little understood and often not accepted by others?

Do we ever insist on defining the supernatural exlusively in terms of our own limited experience, demanding literal acceptance by others? Is this not an approach fully as dangerous as a dogmatic approach to science?

As professing Christians, confronted by a decision of moral or ethical nature, have we ever compromised principle, or have we ever rationalized or shrugged our shoulders at compromise in principle by others?

Have we ever forgotten Christ's counsel—"As you did it to one of the least of these my brethren, you did it to me."

Have we ever been proud when humility would have been more appropriate? Have we ever been belligerent when we should have been compassionate?

Unhappily, we must answer too often in the affirmative, but it is my conviction that the ultimate timing of the renaissance envisioned by Dr. Pollard will largely be determined by our willingness to face the implications of these and other self-critical questions. As Sir Charles Snow said in his address "On Magnanimity":

> For the future is in our hands, if we care enough. The means exist for our seeing to it that the poor of the world don't stay poor. The scientific and technical knowledge which we now possess is enough, if we can find the human means, to solve the problem within a couple of generations. I do not pretend that it is going to be easy to find the human means—but the knowledge exists and, since it exists, no man of the faintest imagination or good will can rest easy.[1]

The supernatural and its spiritual reality do exist, and they will continue to exist without end—our actions and our thoughts can in no way destroy their existence as Dr. Pollard has so clearly stated. But just as surely human

[1] Harper's Magazine, July 1962

action, thought and deed are required if a spiritual rebirth is to take place. God in his infinite wisdom has left it to us to find the human means with which to make a heaven on earth. The supernatural may continue to exist apart, without substantially affecting the human family, or it may burst into our consciousness, enrich our lives, change the course of history.

To a great degree the rapidity with which such a renaissance can come will be determined by those who believe in its possibility, and who by word, deed, thought and conviction prepare the way for it. As we approach Century 21, we who live in Flatland, but who know that another dimension is available to us, have a responsibility to God and to our fellow men, for by the grace of God and our dedicated efforts this new dimension may one day be available to all mankind.

# DISCUSSION ONE

*On each of the first three evenings, the discussion which followed the main addresses was opened by other members of the symposium. They were given the first opportunity to comment either on the addresses or on the evening's theme itself. I have taken the liberty, in editing the transcripts of the discussion, to abbreviate somewhat as well as apply some grammatical hygiene here and there; and I have regretfully omitted most of the asides and jokes as well. What follows contains the pith of the conversation, however.*

DR. WHITE: I've been greatly interested in what has been said [by Mr. Wells] with reference to Dr. Pollard's address, which, to me, was a beautifully delivered sermon. I would like to suggest that perhaps a better title for the symposium these few days might have been "Wisdom and Religion" rather than "Science and Religion," because science as strictly defined is knowledge but not necessarily wisdom, which is the wise application of science or knowledge, and this comes largely with age and experience. Knowledge comes but wisdom lingers. Being one of the senior citizens today, I would like to put in a plug for the senior citizens and express my conviction that if the cerebral circulation remains adequate our senior citizens should be more utilized than they are today!

Finally, just a brief word on Mr. Wells' address. I agree that we can move much faster than we are moving today in improving the spiritual rebirth or renaissance of our country and, as a matter of fact, the whole world. In our international relations as well as our own communities can we not emphasize the brotherhood of man as well as our material aid?

DR. MURPHY: I would perhaps wish to be a little less philosophic and a little more pragmatic about the question of the dependence of man on the supernatural or his concern with it, and why, perhaps, he is less concerned with it in these times than before. It seems to me that man's concern with the supernatural, or rather the device by which he is led to it, religion, really is going to have meaning in the twentieth, twenty-first or the twenty-second century for that matter, only as it has relevance to the people who are living in those times. In the Middle Ages, to which by inference reference was made tonight, western man was enormously concerned with the supernatural. Well, as a matter of fact, he had much reason to be concerned with the supernatural. He knew very little. Most of his children died at birth; his own family had a life expectancy of fifteen or twenty years; he was chronically ill; he was mainly enthralled under serfdom. This temporal life was a very unhappy experience for him from any point of view. It's perfectly clear that anything beyond the present was of enormous relevance to him, and it was no accident that he was concerned with what he could not see and feel, and with the escape from pain and travail.

Now, in the twentieth century, I think the issue is that man finds less relevance in the supernatural. To put it in another way, is it science that has wrapped man in a cocoon to insulate him from the supernatural, or is it that the supernatural has been blurred for him, made obscure for him by those whose job it has been to give him a clear picture of the supernatural? Let me be specific.

The question I would ask, for example is, "Does twentieth-century man believe that, in the recent two or three hundred years to which reference has been made, the Church has been on the side of intellectual freedom, or not?" For certainly intellectual freedom is a very germane matter for modern man, or should be. We declare ourselves to be a free society (and I speak, incidentally, as one who spends most of his days with boys and girls, or men and women from ages eighteen to twenty-five, who are enormously curious about these matters, concerned and seeking). The problem is that no force in our society is going to be very germane to these young people, or have relevance, if it is not a force that stands four-square on the side of intellectual vitality and freedom.

A second question that modern man will ask is, "Has the Church always been a strong force on the side of political freedom?" Those parts of the world today where the supernatural is enormously utilized—utilized for the same reason it was utilized in the Middle Ages—turn to it to escape from temporal tyranny. Has the Church demonstrated its relevance to modern man by being four-square on the side of political freedom, which modern man again has accepted for better or for worse as a fundamental issue?

And then, thirdly, has the Church in these several hundred years to which we have reference, given four-square and outgoing leadership, demonstrating its relevance, by being on the side of social freedom—the freedom of man to stand up, the freedom of man to express in his society human dignity, regardless of race, or color, or creed, or political persuasion? My point is simply this, that no institution that does not demonstrate its strong and positive position, not merely by passive acceptance of these freedoms, but by leadership, courageous even at the expense of a bruise now and then, is going to demonstrate its relevance to these people. And no institution, if it does not demonstrate its relevance, will lead youth into the twenty-first century with the kind of concern for the supernatural to which reference has been made in these papers.

THE MODERATOR: I would like to make one brief remark, following on what Dr. Murphy has just said. The emphasis here has been on the the dominance of science in the twentieth century. It seems to me, however, a case can be made for the statement that we are not really a scientific society. Only relatively few persons, and those in relatively small areas of their lives, are searching for evidence, and postponing judgment until all the facts are in. In fact, in many ways, this is a religious age. Although many of us are not impressed by the quality of the religion, we certainly have to be impressed by the quantity of it. The need, I think, today is not simply to appeal for a return of interest in spiritual values, but to think through what it is to be religious in the kind of world we live in. Part of our religious flabbiness (if I may use that term) is, I think, a result of our lack of knowledge of the kind of world we live in— our lack of true scientific knowledge. More emphasis on science so that we really know the facts that we are dealing with and the kinds of real problems that human beings struggle with—more knowledge of the real condition of man—is what we need to be truly religious in the rest of this century.

PROF. YINGER: I am grateful for the last two speakers. Dr. Pollard's prophecy that man will return to the supernatural or to religion in the twenty-first century reminded me of the prophecy of Oswald Spengler in his book *The Decline of the West.* He proclaimed the end of the age of reason, and the coming of an age of faith. And many of the theologians in the west were naive enough to believe that he meant it to be a good religion and a good faith.

The age of reason died in many places in western civilization; but it was replaced by demonic religion—Nazism, Communism. Therefore I am grateful for the insistence on the form of the religious revival. If there is to be one in the twentieth and twenty-first century depends largely upon the vitality and the relevance of a particular type of religion in the contests of religions good and bad. I am grateful to Dr. Murphy for reminding us that we Christians not only believe in Original Sin, but we practise it!

*At this point, the three "reactors" were asked to join in the dialogue.*

FR. FRENSDORFF: Part of my question, I think, has already been raised in the discussion. But I wonder, Dr. Pollard, whether you intend by what struck me as a very optimistic view of the future, thereby to ignore the crisis in which many of us, or most of us, I think, feel we live at this moment—the very critical state of our society, in terms of

some of the problems that Dr. Murphy mentioned, to say
nothing of the threat of extinction as we set off a few more
blasts to which science has helped us. I mean the moral im-
peratives, the moral problems that most of us take very
seriously, and not only in this room. Your address seems
to ignore these and point us to a rosy future. My question
is, "Does this 'rosy future' come about by God's patient
action—if we wait long enough—in His economy, or is it
because man's spirit will eventually 'bust open' and bring
about this renaissance; is there a witness to which we are
called at this very moment?"

DR. POLLARD: Well, let's see how I would take these. I am
fully aware of the moral concern both you and Dr.
Murphy express. We all need to be more profoundly concerned with the role of the Church in just this year, this
moment, in protecting the freedoms that have been so long
and terribly fought for; and undoubtedly the Church falls
down in many ways. And I don't mean not to plead for
immediate action in so far as we can take it. But we can't
change the quality of a culture overnight. This never happens in human history. We can't change the dominant
passions of our age in a moment. Dr. Murphy mentioned
the Middle Ages. He seems to me to have given rather a
gloomy view of them, and I think a somewhat unfair one.
It is as though they were being criticized for not having
produced modern medicine and public health measures,
and modern argriculture, etc. I think that in God's unfolding providence in history, that was not the role of the Middle Ages. Anyhow, it didn't happen until much later!

I also wonder how miserable and agonizing life really
was. I don't mean that I'm not immensely grateful for

blood transfusions, for antibiotics, for all the wonders, and the great helps of modern medicine and all of modern science. But I am not at all sure that people are so much happier and less miserable now than they were in the Middle Ages. This is the age of tranquilizers, of horrible anxieties and fears, of deep problems of alcoholism, of every type of problem. You get rid of one terrible problem of human existence and a dozen others crop up. It's like ridding the house of one evil spirit, and if you don't put anything else in its place, then seven spirits more wicked than the first enter in and take over.

And finally, I'm not pleading for the supernatural as if it were a pill the world could take. It's not as though I'm saying "this is what the world needs now." It's just that I believe that there are ranges of reality that men have known through the ages, and that today we have lost the capacity to know. We are in one kind of dark age. And I don't believe this kind of dark age is going to last. I'm not pleading for a change, I'm just trying to interpret. I don't know how fast it will happen. It would be nice if it would just suddenly happen; but I don't believe that we can control the rate of a renaissance of rediscovery. I don't think there is much we can do about that but wait and rejoice as it comes—become a part of it and let it develop.

Now, if the world ends before the twenty-first century, I don't know—I don't have any words of wisdom to give on how to stop it from ending before the twenty-first century. I don't mean that there aren't moral concerns. To me, these are not uppermost. It's the structure of reality that is important, and we should operate and make our moral decisions within a certain framework of what we regard as real and important. And if our framework is restricted or wrong or cut off, then all of our moral decisions, all of our orientations to what to decide and what we're passionate about and what we desire or want, are all wrong. That is the point.

Miss Jenkins: Dr. Pollard, you say that the Resurrection is the most important fact of all history for man to know and respond to. You also said that to learn something of heaven and eternity one has to turn to the religious heritage of the West. I would like to ask two questions. In the face of our present competition and conflict with the non-western world, do you see Christianity as the only means towards this rediscovery and renaissance? In other words, is this a movement of the western world alone? If so, what of the great religions and the great numbers of people of other cultures and their effect on this development? And second, a practical question, how can the Church and its schools help? Indeed, what is the role of the public schools in hastening the day that you see ahead?

Dr. Pollard: Well, let me take those up in order. First of all, as to the role of other religions beyond the Judaeo-Christian, in the rediscovery of the reality of something more than space, time, and matter, I think they have a tremendous role to play. India, China, and Japan—they, just as much as the western world, have had this intuitive, this really human, sense of realities transcendent to the realities which are investigated by science; and perhaps when science is transplanted to those cultures, the relationship between the natural and that which transcends nature will reappear.

But I will say this, that the world transcendent to space

and time which has been recognized by every culture from the most primitive up to now has largely been an enigma. It even was pretty much of an enigma in Judaism, as one can tell from the Old Testament. To be sure, much about it was revealed within the life and history of Israel that shaped it up in a coherent manner. Nevertheless, the key event of the Resurrection and all that it implied—that the supernatural, the ultimate reality upon which the whole of the space-time universe depends, has become incarnate on this earth within our history—"The word was made flesh, and dwelt among us"—this blinding illumination of the nature of the transcendent is absolutely unique. Compared to it, Hinduism, or Buddhism, which is scarcely a religion, makes no pretense to reveal any transcendent reality—certainly not the nature of God.

All of these others are obscure and tentative. They're full of the demonic. Dr. Yinger pointed this out. Just "religion" itself isn't necessarily a good thing at all. It can be quite a bad thing. In many primitive cultures religion can be a horrible force to hold man down and depress him and imprison him. And I deeply believe that these great events—the Resurrection, the Incarnation, the life, Crucifixion, death and Ascension of the Lord Jesus Christ—are real events in the real history of the world. Thereby, they aren't just a "religion"; they're something that actually happened, that profoundly illuminates the supernatural domain. And without that light, one just struggles in darkness still. But at least, whether illumined or not, people of cultures other than the twentieth-century scientific culture, have at least had some capacity to believe something real was there. And we've even lost that. That's my thesis.

Now, let's see, what was the other question? . . . oh yes, the schools. I made the statement in my talk, that one of the major pieces of evidence of the extent to which we have lost this capacity for the supernatural is the character of our whole educational process. It is hard to change the character of this. People should teach what they believe. If they don't do that, we really are lost. Every teacher must be true to himself or herself. In that sense the culture transmits itself; and this provides a long delay in any really fundamental change in the basic convictions that are transmitted in the educational process.

But it is changing. Teachers change. For example, I had already left the university before I changed in any material way. But still, I teach, and I have contact with people; and little by little others are catching this fire; and that's the way a renaissance slowly develops. Here and there individuals infected with a new vision begin transmitting it. They can't help themselves. Now, I don't see how we can mastermind this process. I don't see how we can develop any scheme to make it go much faster. But it is happening. And I just sense it's going to happen more. I don't believe it will be confined to Church schools, or secular schools. I doubt seriously that that makes a great deal of difference. At least in my experience—and I've been to a lot of Church schools of all kinds of affiliation, and to state schools, state universities—I don't see any difference in the reality that each transmits to our youngsters, not any material difference. This is something culture-wide and deep within us. It's going to take time. Whether we have enough time or not—that's up to the Lord, not up to me. In other words, there are limits to what we ourselves can do about this.

MR. MORRIS: One of Dr. Pollard's main points was that this age would be the golden age of science, implying that the pace will slacken, that the next age will live on the fruits of this. I might point out that something like this prediction was made in 1885 by a German physicist who said that everything to be discovered in science had been discovered, and all that was necessary now was to fill in the gaps. It was about five or ten years later, as I remember, that electrons and radioactivity and that sort of thing showed up. And I'm just wondering if there isn't the perfectly good possibility of entirely new break-throughs in fields that we know nothing about, so that the pace, rather than slackening, will become even more hectic in the next age? However, these are very minor criticisms.

It seems to me, though, that there is a major point that hasn't been made tonight, which is summed up in Dr. Pollard's statement—a perfectly correct statement—that science is the study of the natural, and more or less implying that we must look away from this to the supernatural. This he probably did not say and I'm quite sure he did not mean. For it is very important to realize that if you start thinking in these terms you are completely losing the point of Christianity. The whole point of Christianity is that it is through the natural that we can know the supernatural. Therefore, in making this separation, which it seems to me has implicitly been made, between the natural and the supernatural, we are being un-Christian. Christianity itself, let's say, began to come back into its own when its history began to be studied scientifically, when the historians themselves started to try to track things down with all the accuracy and all the tools of modern science. In the same way Christians say that this world is the manifestation of the supernatural world, and that it is only through what we know in this world that we can know of the supernatural world. The whole concept of the sacramental comes in here. So that rather than implying that there should be a turning-the-emphasis-away from the natural and toward the supernatural, it seems to me that the importance in the next century, or whenever this crystal ball event takes place, must be in seeing the natural as the manifestation of the supernatural—seeing the natural as the sacramental presentation. It is only through what we see in this world that we can know of God.

DR. WHITE: May I add a brief comment about the Church and the supernatural? In 1705, during a very cold winter in Rome, there were many sudden deaths. And the people of Rome were very much alarmed and began to leave Rome because they were sure that God was angry with them. This epidemic was considered "supernatural." But the Pope, Clement XI, and his very wise physician, Lancissi, decided they must combat this superstition. So the Pope requested autopsies to find out whether the cause of death was natural or supernatural. The Church itself requested autopsies; and Lancissi carried them out following the next sudden deaths during the winter of 1705-6; and in every case a natural cause, an easily-discovered cause, for the death was found, usually arterial disease. But, in the preface to the book which was published (*On Sudden Death*), by Lancissi, dedicated to Pope Clement XI, he said, "And the Pope, adding prudence to piety, appointed a committee"!

THE MODERATOR: I would so much like to agree with this last comment about the material, natural characteristic of the Christian revelation. It is in sacramental form that the supernatural is made manifest in the natural. But I don't mean to suggest that we abandon our interest in the natural. It isn't an either/or matter. We don't have any direct access to any reality beyond the natural. I want us to hang on to the natural, and I'm sure we will. And let there not be any kind of sharp dividing line. They are completely intermingled (to go back to our analogy), just as Flatland is completely immersed in space; and they completely intersect each other at every point. That is the relation; there is no sharp boundary. It isn't that you have to be completely and wholeheartedly and passionately devoted to the natural in exclusion to anything else beside it, or wholeheartedly and passionately devoted to the supernatural and forget all the natural. Why can't we have the whole of reality and not just a part of it?

Mr. Morris: If there were an implication here that Dr. Pollard or I were trying to separate the natural from the supernatural, I would like to dispel that assumption. We do need both. They go together. They depend upon each other. As to the timing of such a renaissance, I don't think I'm an optimist—at least by my definition of an optimist. I think an optimist is someone who thinks something good is going to happen automatically. I think, as Dr. Pollard said, this will take time. It will take devotion and dedication. I think it will come, but I think we have to take part in it. Something happened this morning, when we were going up the Space Needle. We got in that sort of endless maze, and the attendant said, "the sooner you get in line, the sooner you will go up!"

The Moderator: Our time is ending, and I'm afraid I must attempt some kind of summary of our conversation.

I feel what Dr. Pollard feels—indeed we all felt it, as our spontaneous response to him indicated—the sense of our imprisonment within the natural and our need for release. I remember dimly a quotation from—I think it was Ortega —who said that he wondered whether sufficient thought had ever been given to the number of things that must be kept alive in the human spirit if the spirit of science was to survive. That is another way of commenting on precisely this same problem. Much more is needed than simply the spirit or the technique or the abilities of science, if science itself in any pure and creative form is to remain alive. And I rather think that Dr. Pollard would have joined in that.

We are not choosing between either/or's. We are all reaching after a wider frontier of thought and spirit—or perhaps, to say it another way, we are all reaching toward a language which is more nearly a universal language, one that will permit us to talk with one another about the things of time and space and about the things which are not of time and space. This may be the heart of our problem in our time.

One final comment which I should make. I am elderly, stuffy-minded, and also cynical. I do not think that anybody is completely and always "right." I do not think that there has ever been any "right" time to live. I don't think there ever will be. I think that when the clergy run the world, we make it an impossible place. Dr. Murphy spoke with feeling about what a clerical world was like, and he was dead right about it. I also have the same feeling about a scientific society. I do not like scientific clericalists any more than Episcopalian clericalists.

My point in all this is the absolute necessity, when we

are, as we are now, at this most central and critical turning point, of our keeping some sense of humor and perspective about all this. Nobody is right; there never was a time when we had the right balance of things in the world; and there's no use waiting for such a time because you'll wait forever, and then you'll be astonished by the supernatural! Our time is now and our choices are now. It's in this world that we've got to live and bear our witness as to the things which need saying and doing. We are indeed whole-hearted believers in the sacramental. The man of science, the liberal spirit of whatever persuasion, is likely to be suspicious of the sacramentalist as such; he says that the sacramentalist can feel very holy about a piece of bread, and he wishes that he would feel something of the same holiness about a man. This is a legitimate criticism about us, when our small sacramentalisms smother the greatness of the human spirit and of the work of God.

We are not against sacramentalism! We only need to remember that there is a sacramentalism which applies to bread and wine, and also and equally the same sacramentalism applies to the person to whom you give the cup of cold water and discover you are giving it to Christ. Now it is in this latter sense that we have so often failed. When the Church spoke of the supernatural, we were understood to be speaking of little, priestly, parlor tricks. The real supernatural at the heart of the Church is the heroic devotion of people to people and to their Lord, expressed in martyrdom, expressed in love, expressed in the endless willingness to put man first, ahead of all the sub-human things. And when the Church speaks in these terms we are not misunderstood.

# II

# THE BIOLOGICAL SCIENCES

DR. PAUL DUDLEY WHITE
DR. FRANKLIN MURPHY

*Discussion "Reactors":*

Mrs. Howard M. Heckedorn
Dr. Robert Barnes
The Rev. Matthew Bigliardi

# The Biological Sciences

## Dr. Paul Dudley White

*Bishop Bayne, my fellow panelists, ladies and gentlemen:*
I appreciate very much your kind invitation to visit
Seattle again, where I have so many friends, in order to
take part in this Symposium on Science and Religion. As
a physician, I have had many friends and patients among
both the scientists and the clergy and I am happy to say
that I have found them all to be very much alike, as human
beings, in all parts of the world. But after listening to the
debate last evening I am even more content than I was
before that most of my work deals with "natural" phenomena, including even the spirit of man and not with the
*supernatural*. However, I suspect that some of you around
me may have the opposite satisfaction. I would end these
introductory remarks by quoting a favorite phrase,
namely: "*Men's* lives are chains of chances . . ." and I
rather suspect that there are natural rather than supernatural backgrounds of those chances.

A point that may help to explain some of the things
which I shall say is that I am to all intents and purposes a
Unitarian. And now let me present my address itself.

Literally *Biological Sciences* means the *Sciences of the
Science of Life*. Actually what we mean is two-fold: in the

first place, the vital issue itself, namely the origin and other aspects of life; and in the second place, knowledge about living matter. By definition again life itself is depicted by Webster's Dictionary as that quality or character distinguishing an animal or a plant from inorganic or from dead organic bodies, which is especially manifested by metabolism, growth, reproduction, and internal powers of adaptation to environment.

*The Origin of Life*—The biochemists and the biophysicists through their researches appear to be on the edge of the artificial creation of life, but so far the vital spark eludes them. Here the mystery remains. Some believe that it should remain so, that here is the Holy of Holies, but God Himself, for all we know, may wish us to solve this mystery as we have already solved other mysteries through the inventive mind of man. Such discoveries and inventions as the microscope and the telescope, electricity and its harnessing, the flying machine, radio and television, the splitting of the atom, the theory of evolution, drugs to cure disease, the intricacies of the human brain, and the interdependence of the psyche and the soma would once have been and actually were regarded as heresy to be punished by excommunication or death. Nowadays most of us who have had ourselves a taste of new knowledge believe that we should stop at nothing except what we all recognize as evil, like wars, inhumanity to man or beast, and the breaking of the Ten Commandments. But knowledge about the unknown should be sought as an obligation of mankind.

*The Sanctity of Life*—Before I leave this consideration of life itself, that is, the act of living, I would like to discuss two other debated problems, namely, the sanctity of life itself and immortality. How sacred should we consider life? From the beginning of recorded history and doubtless earlier still, it has been both convention and law that human life is sacred and must not be destroyed except in wars called "holy" to condone such bloodshed. One of the Ten Commandments, "Thou shalt not kill," was the rule of all civilization for many centuries before the birth of Christ and continues to be our rule today. Although, moreover, euthanasia has every so often been proposed to relieve the suffering of "hopelessly ill" or dying invalids it has not been accepted for a variety of reasons. But how far should the sanctity of life extend to other animals and to the vegetable kingdom? Should insects, even those that carry or can carry disease, and plant life be held as sacred, as has been the teaching of some philosophers, except as "the extinction of such life is essential for the survival of man"? But is not this exception in itself a contradiction, a selfish point of view of this philosophy? I don't know how far this concept of the sanctity of life extends in the minds of such proponents thereof—does it include the life of microorganisms dangerous to man himself?

*Immortality*—"The spirit lives; all else is mortal," are the words inscribed on the pedestal of which rests the bony elbow supporting the bony skull of the handsome skeleton in the first woodcut of the famous Anatomy of Vesalius published in 1543. This is, I believe, the teaching of religions the world over. But how can we best interpret the first three words—The spirit lives? We have no proof that life as we have defined it in my opening paragraph survives after death or that the spirit or personality can survive by itself in any heaven, hell, or purgatory; but anyone and everyone must admit that the spirit can and often does, for better or for worse, survive in the lives of others, often as yet unborn, through the direct effect of living example, or by its indirect effect by the spoken or by the written word. The lives of great men and of great women have in this way become immortal throughout the ages in every walk of life, but especially in their religious precepts. Such immortals in Christianity, Judaism, and the Moslem faith are of course the prophets, in particular Moses with his tables, David with his Psalms, Christ with his Sermon on the Mount, His Parables, and His many other wonderful teachings, and Mohammed with his Koran. These and others exemplifying not religion per se but rather science, the arts including music, and statesmanship are the Immortals. And one other truth thus becomes manifest that *this*, which I believe is the only immortality that exists, must be achieved in this life, not in the "next."

Let us turn now to the more concrete aspects of biology or the knowledge of life, the growing edge of which is ever expanding more and more rapidly. For convenience we may consider it best under four headings: (1) microbiology, the science of minute vegetable and animal life, including the single cell, whether isolated or incorporated, (2) visible vegetation, (3) visible animal life, and (4) cosmobiology, that is, biology through outer space, also still invisible to us.

(1) *Microbiology*—Our science of the invisible really began with Leeuwenhoek whom Paul de Kruif so vividly brought to life in his book entitled *The Microbe Hunters*, published 36 years ago. I can heartily recommend to you the reading of Chapter One in that book. Let me quote a brief passage:

Peering through his own hand-made microscope at a drop of water, he exclaimed: "There are little animals in this rainwater. They swim! They play! They are a thousand times smaller than any creatures we can see with our eyes alone."[1]

There are still many mysteries to solve in microbiology: for example, what new unicellular organisms are being born and under what circumstances? How do these minute forms of life evolve and change either to become different or to become more fully developed in themselves or to grow into multicellular structures and how rapidly? Recently at the Eighth International Cancer Congress in Moscow, I heard a very interesting report by a Swedish investigator, Dr. Audrey Fjelde, of a ten-year study of three long-lived tissue cultures. The cells in the culture remained unchanged throughout the ten years unless she introduced a disturbing factor, in this case viruses, which distorted the morphology, that is, the shape of their cells, and their number of chromosomes. Then, if she added nothing more, they retained these newly acquired characteristics for generations to come. Another, now well-recognized, change has been that of the development of acquired resistance of certain bacteria to certain antibiotics. Finally, in the May 25th issue of *Science* there is a fascinating article by S. E. Luria entitled "Bacteriophage Genes and Bacterial Functions." His conclusions were as follows:

This brief survey of bacteriophage infection has provided support for an obvious but important generalization: that the study of virus infection at the cellular level is a branch of cellular genetics. The interactions between viral and cellular functions show that infection with a virus is not just a disrupting intrusion; it is an addition to the cellular endowment

[1] The Microbe Hunters, by Paul de Kruif, text edited by Harry G. Grover (Harcourt, Brace & Co., New York, 1932).

of genetic specificity. The outcome of this addition depends on the nature of the instructions carried by the viral genome, on the ability of the cellular machinery to carry out these instructions, and on the availability of control mechanisms to regulate the functions of the added element.

Inevitably, the most easily recognized viruses are those that produce destructive events in their hosts. Even these destructive effects of virus infections are exerted at the genetic rather than at the metabolic level, contrary to the situation in infectious diseases caused by bacteria and other pathogens. This viewpoint need not foster pessimism in the search for practical approaches to the control of virus diseases, such as antiviral chemotherapy; it simply means that the solutions will probably be quite different from those applicable to other types of infectious diseases.

It may well be that in order to cure virus diseases we may first have to learn to affect selectively the intimate processes of gene function and regulation. Progress in this area of biology is proceeding at a tremendous rate. Virologists find it rewarding to know that virus research is a major contributor to current developments in molecular biology.[1]

These are but instances of our growing knowledge of the microscopic life around us and yet we have barely scratched its surface.

(2) *Botany*—Here is an old and well established scientific field on which the very existence of the life of the animal kingdom and the basic facts of evolution are dependent. During the nineteenth century much of the pioneering in genetics and in the mode of inheritance was carried out on plants by Mendel, Darwin, and other explorers at that time. Much earlier indeed, by over a century (1733), the understanding of hydrodynamics of living things had been initiated by Stephen Hales in England in his studies of the sap of trees as well as of the blood pressure of a mare.

[1] Reprinted from *Science* by permission

Since animal life survives largely because of its ingestion of living plants, it becomes apparent that the surface of our globe is extremely variable in its ability to support animal life except as food is brought into some otherwise uninhabitable area. The development of agriculture through the clearing of forests by primitive man and further advances by irrigation and the building of dams, along with the introduction of more expert fertilization and the control of insect pests and of virus diseases of plant life have, in addition to the prevention and control of infectious diseases in man, allowed humanity to multiply manifold during the last century. This threat of overpopulation has greatly stimulated efforts to discover the most suitable methods of birth control and the education of the masses to accept them. The wisdom of at least some limitation of the size of families is slowly gaining converts but an ideal solution still eludes us.

Another current problem demanding solution is that of the overproduction of food like wheat or rice in certain countries with the expense and waste of its storage while other countries are in need of these very supplies.

Still another problem involving plant life is that of the need of reforestation in many parts of the world to combat the evil effects of the destruction of the forests by improvident man. Happily this is now in progress here and there as its need becomes more and more evident.

(3) *Animal Life*—Many thousands of volumes could be and have been written on the many aspects of animal life and yet it is my task in this brief paper to present to you for the purpose of this symposium a few succinct problems that concern us as humans.

Some of the things that I mentioned under the heading

of the vegetable kingdom are equally applicable to animal life, in particular its adaptation to its physical environment, its survival of the fittest, and its relation as a whole to man as an individual. How can we conserve for their own good, but especially for our own welfare, an optimal distribution and utilization of the myriads of genera and of species of animals, large and small, spread over the surface of the earth, in the seas about us, and in the air above? In this respect we are already fortunate in that our ancestors initiated the many scientific specialties that deal with individual problems. To name a few, we have first, the highly developed but still growing discipline of entomology, which concerns insects and in particular our own relationship to them. Some of these insects are harmful to man in that they destroy our buildings (the termites), our clothes (the moths), or our food (the locusts, for example), or spread disease, such as the anopheles mosquito (malaria), the tse-tse fly (sleeping sickness), and the louse (exanthematic typhus fever). Other insects are of great value, such as the silkworm, the honeybee, and the lowly earthworm. Even the cockroach, said to be the most ancient survivor of the animal kingdom, is doubtless a useful scavenger. From time to time, especially when wars, floods, and epidemics of disease have threatened to exterminate mankind, it has been said that our successors as masters of this planet will be the insects. Meanwhile they remain both a blessing to man, and a menace.

Other scientific specialties dealing with animal life include ornithology, oceanography and ichthyology, animal husbandry, the preservation of wildlife, veterinary medicine, anthropology and genetics, and the many branches of the study of man himself (physical, mental, and spiritual), both in health and in disease. As I have already said myriads of treatises have been written dealing with each of these special fields and I can do no more than refer to a few cogent problems that may be particularly appropriate to this symposium on Science and Religion.

One of the ever recurring subjects for contemplation and discussion is that of the prevention of cruelty to animals, including humans, children and adults alike. The "humane" killing of animals for food has become an accepted way of life, and on occasion it is, of course, necessary for our very existence as humans to destroy dangerous or superfluous wild life, but the senseless slaughter of animals for the so-called "fun of it" is to be deprecated. On the other hand, a cult of so-called anti-vivisectionists has gone so far as to oppose and actually to obstruct the needed scientific advance of medicine through the use, as humanely as possible, of experimental animals. Much of the spectacular treatment, both medical and surgical, of the present day has come through animal study and experimentation. Many thousands of human patients are alive and well today who would have died hopelessly crippled in their infancy, childhood, or early adult life had it not been possible to make these animal studies. This is true, for example, of severe diabetes, of a considerable number of deformities and diseases of the heart and blood vessels, cured or greatly helped by operations, and of a host of ills that can be effectively treated by drugs which must first be tested on animals. This, of course, assumes that man is to be regarded as the prime living creature.

Now let us turn to this superior animal, man himself, in health and in disease in all his aspects, physical, mental, and spiritual. The whole man must be so considered and, although this obvious precept is not always observed, the experienced physician, educator, and churchman in his practice, in his teaching, and in his research should always act accordingly. At this point I would, with or without your permission, discard the word *psyche* because it has come to mean two different things which, although doubtless related and resident together in the brain, are not the same. These two meanings are (1) the *mind*, which is a combination of thoughts, secretions of the brain as it were, and (2) the *soul* or spirit or personality, a different attribute of man entirely, although also resident in the brain. The greater development of the brain in man is responsible for his greater mental capacity and his more distinctive spiritual qualities, good or bad, although some animals, including the dog and doubtless the monkey too, do develop striking personalities.

I am sure that the thoughtful physician is interested in more than the physical condition of his patient, the genuine educator heeds more than the mental state, and the dedicated minister more than his spirituality. But too often the appraisal and the treatment is one-sided and there is frequently a tendency to over-emphasize one or another of these three sides of man at the expense of the other two. The only reason why I shall mention the word *psyche* once more is with reference to so-called psychosomatic physiology and medicine in which either or both of the special functions of the human brain, that is, mind and spirit, influence the body itself either helpfully or harmfully. There is no doubt whatsoever that the positive virtues of courage, patience, equanimity, optimism, and kindness, can beneficially act upon the human organism, both in health and in disease, while the opposite attributes of fear, impatience,

anger, pessimism, and unkindness can and do have a harmful effect on man's body as well as on his mind and soul.
And let me add in closing this reference to the psyche,
that the interaction is bilateral, and that the body, that is,
the soma, has a very important influence on both the mind
and the soul; this is "somatopsychic physiology and
medicine." The body is indeed "the handmaid or the
temple of the soul".

It is my function this evening, I am sure, to stress in
particular bodily health and disease in man and their direct
relationship to mental and spiritual health and disease. My
own special field in medicine concerns the circulation of
blood and you will hear shortly how that is related to the
health of the whole man, a relationship the emphasis on
which may be my most useful contribution to medical
science.

When I was a medical student and a young doctor we
were struggling to control the many serious infectious
diseases which filled our hospitals and were the prime
causes of a heavy mortality in youth and middle age
throughout the whole world. Such deaths were considered
inevitably the will of God, that is, supernatural. I witnessed
helplessly literally thousands of deaths from typhoid fever,
pneumonia, infantile dysentery, meningitis, exanthematic
typhus, rheumatic fever, diphtheria, and tuberculosis. A
few infections such as cholera, leprosy, and yellow fever,
although rampant in many parts of the world, no longer
reached New England, although my father's mother died
as a very young woman of cholera in one of the last epidemics brought to America.

During the last forty-odd years the medical scene in
New England has changed completely. Infections still

occur, but much less frequently and they are usually cured by the antibiotics of today. The hospitals are now full of much older patients but most of them are still too young to die as they do. The conditions that they suffer from mostly now are in the order of their frequency: mental diseases, arteriosclerosis, arthritis, cancer, and accidents. Three of these together are the cause of three quarters of all the deaths in the U.S.A. today. In the order of their importance in mortality arteriosclerosis ranks first, being responsible for 50 to 55 per cent of all deaths, cancer second, causing 16 per cent, and accidents third, causing 5 per cent. Tuberculosis which accounted for more deaths than any other cause forty years ago is now far down the list, being responsible for less than one per cent (0.6 per cent).

Following the custom of the early years of the present century one might say that these current deaths, so often occurring in youth and middle age, are still supernatural, that is the "Act of God." We know better now. They are obviously our fault, but with adequate money, energy, and determination we should within the next generation be able to control them sufficiently at least to extend our longevity from the Biblical average of three score and ten years today to at least four score. And it is not simply adding years to life but *also health to those years.*

In closing this third section of my discourse let me take as an example of human health and disease what I know best, namely the circulation of blood. It is important to recognize first some simple facts in human physiology that are widely neglected in this age of complicated biochemical and biophysical researches. It has been known for hundreds of years that the veins of the extremities have valves. William Harvey in the early 1600s demonstrated that the blood *must* circulate because these valves when competent prevent the blood from falling back away from the heart. The valves are especially important in the leg veins where gravity tends to produce a stasis of blood with man in the standing or sitting position. Of equal importance with these valves in the veins is the tone and contraction of the muscles of the extremities, especially those of the legs which work against gravity to help to pump blood back to the heart, the lungs, and the brain. Hence good condition of the large leg muscles, kept fit by regular and vigorous use, is a very important factor in maintaining a good circulation in man *beneficial to clear thinking and a good spirit*. Thus the heart, though of course the most essential part of the circulatory tract, is much helped by several accessory factors, two of which I have just named, the valves of the veins and good tone of the leg muscles. Two other aids to the circulation of blood are: 1) good, that is, normal elasticity of the great artery, the aorta, and of its largest branches, and 2) good tone and free motion of the diaphragm, a powerful muscle, which makes of the thorax a suction pump for blood as well as for air.

It becomes evident from these simple physiological facts that fitness of the circulation depends in considerable measure on general physical fitness of the musculature of the body, grossly neglected today by the great majority of our middle-aged citizens, some of whom are inclined to scoff at the idea of trying to maintain a state of positive health, not just the absence of disease.

Perhaps most important of all in this advice for the establishment and maintenance of physical fitness by labor or by substituted exercise (and here the laborer has an advantage in that the vigorous use of his muscles is a part of his daily work) is its bearing on the circulation to the brain at the top of the human frame and its antidotal value in combatting nervous and emotional stress and strain and insomnia. Physical (that is, muscular) fatigue is the best tranquilizer and hypnotic when properly balanced. During one's waking hours it is probable that one can think more clearly while walking at a pleasant pace and without distraction as the stoic or promenading philosophers apparently found out centuries before Christ when they met at the Athenian Agora. A proper balancing of mental and of physical effort is the ideal program for upright man as he is constructed today. He is not yet all brain or all body either, as some would have us believe.

And, even more important still, the spirit or personality of man which also resides in the brain along with our mental function, is optimally developed and utilized if our cerebral circulation is at its best.

I have stressed these simple but vital physiological and psychological facts because they have not been adequately presented by the medical profession, including many physicians who are among the worst offenders. Such physicians are often extremely able in the diagnosis and in the treatment of disease, but neglectful of health, including their own in particular. In contrast obesity is a well recognized though often more difficult problem to solve. It is known to be a bar to optimal health and does shorten life as a rule, but physical indolence needs also to be emphasized. Quite naturally the two often go together.

Physical educators, of this country in particular, have been inadequately esteemed, partly because of the faddists among them who have commercially or otherwise exploited the field and partly because of our general ignorance of the role which the more scientific among them should fulfill. A fortnight ago in the laboratories and swimming pools and on the exercise fields of the Sports Stadium in Moscow I had the pleasure of visiting Professor Letounov and his staff and of learning of their useful work.

And now before ending this next to the last chapter of my address I come to the most common fatal disease of all, which today cuts short so many lives and which is responsible for most of the heart attacks, many of the strokes, and much of the high blood pressure which we see around us. This is the type of arteriosclerosis which we call *atherosclerosis*, a rusting of the inner lining of the arteries to heart muscle, to brain, to kidneys, to leg muscles, and to other tissues and organs of the body with the resulting obstruction to blood flow. There are still mysteries about this disease to solve and much more research to support, but we are finding that in addition to a factor of heredity, *an overrich diet and a physically inactive life* favor an earlier development of serious atherosclerosis in our middle-aged men today, men whose usefulness, health, and happiness should continue for many more years than is now the situation. It is not "God's will," that is, supernatural, that a man of 45 years of age should die suddenly, or have a heart attack, or suffer a stroke. It is our fault, that is, a natural error.

This then is a simple message of mine, but a very vital one, I am sure, to many of my educational and clerical colleagues who have not yet put it into practice either for others or for themselves.

(4) *Cosmobiology*—Finally, I would add a word or

two about life elsewhere in the universe or rather in infinite space. As Harlow Shapley and others have believed, it is extremely likely that there are many worlds like ours in the galaxies in space, and therein microorganisms, plants, and animals like our own, in fact humans too quite probably, variably advanced in their development of a civilized state. Even though we haven't yet heard from them, they too may be beginning to explore space. In other universes, as well as in our own, there may be worlds with life not at all like ours because of different living conditions. It hardly seems likely, however, that our planets nearest and farthest from the sun could support life as we know it. But before we spend too much time and effort out of this world we have more than enough pressing and exciting problems to solve right here at home. Let me cite one such problem which has fascinated me and which was recently suggested in an international connotation by President Kennedy; namely, the need of the replacement of, or addition to, the Declaration of Independence of man by a Declaration of the Interdependence of man, or even of his dependence on so much else in this universe of ours. Man cannot exist as a being apart. Nevertheless, it is my conviction that the individuality of every human being needs to be recognized as such and to be safe-guarded, not to be lost through any doctrine of obliteration as an unimportant speck of any mass of humanity, whether national or international.

May I close with a time-honored, but much neglected, injunction which is, with little doubt, a most vital need in our human biology today, and a clear solution to all of our many cold wars, if it can be put into actual practice, as I believe should someday be possible: *Love Thy Neighbor as Thyself.* This most important weapon for the ending of world strife, namely, love of our fellow man with understanding of his problems and infinite patience, transcends even the Golden Rule and is by far the best basis for treaties, economic unions, and world law, all of which can then easily follow. *But without such love and understanding all else is insecure.*

Thank you for letting me present to you something of the vast area of our knowledge and also of our ignorance of that fascinating science which we call *life.*

# Faith and Reason
# in an Age of Discovery

Dr. Franklin D. Murphy

IN MAN'S endless struggle to negotiate the difficult path from barbarism and darkness to civilization and light, two forces, *reason* and *faith*, have played major and often conflicting roles. Even in the faint traces of prehistoric man these elements are present. Basic animal curiosity, associated with the power of observation and coordinated by a much advanced brain, made possible the extraordinary cave paintings of Cro-Magnon man in southern France and northern Spain. Yet, it seems clear that a concern with the supernatural motivated these artists to make their drawings some 25,000 years ago.

From the beginning man wished to know more about himself and his environment, and he was moved to use his unique human tools to this end. Yet, he needed an explanation of the vast areas of the unknown, and, lacking it, he turned to the supernatural.

At the outset man applied his curiosity in unplanned and perhaps almost reflex fashion. But, as his experience grew, so did his body of knowledge and therefore his power to reason. Thus, casual curiosity became planned investigation, and the attack on the area of the unknown proceeded apace.

At the same time man's increasing sophistication led him to make more formal and organized his dependence on the supernatural. This formalizing, which we call religion, took a variety of forms but always with two major objectives: (1) the setting down of principles, ethical and otherwise, by which man lives and associates with his fellows and (2) the exploration of the great unanswered questions of self and environment. As the several faiths developed maturity, they predictably tended to develop ever more precise and rigid canons of ethics and beliefs about the unanswered questions, related, of course, to the intellectual and social realities of the time. Yet, simultaneously, man's power of reason was maturing and the area of the unknown shrinking. It was then inevitable that established religious belief would come into conflict with newly established facts on the one hand and our changing social order on the other. Although no culture or religion has been immune to this phenomenon, we are most familiar with the problem as it occurred in Western civilization and in relation to the Judaeo-Christian ethic.

Toward the end of the Middle Ages, the Christian faith was in deep philosophical difficulty adjusting to the science of Aristotle. It was left to that towering figure, Thomas Aquinas, to build a bridge to surmount this crisis. It was a remarkable bridge. Yet, it was not strong enough to support Galileo when, in the sixteenth century, he made discoveries relating to the universe which were in conflict with established religious doctrine. In more recent times we recall the acrimonious exchanges between Huxley and Bishop Wilberforce (or, if you prefer, between Clarence

Darrow and William Jennings Bryan) concerning the validity of Charles Darwin's theories of the evolution of man. Indeed, the echoes of this scientific-religious conflict are heard down to the present day.

In the heat of these ideological struggles, objectivity often gave way to emotion. Terms such as heretic, unethical, anti-Christ and atheist were flung about with abandon and usually quite inaccurately. We know, for example, that Galileo was in fact a most religious man and that he felt deeply dependent upon the inspiration of God for his discoveries. The observers of man and nature have never been, in the main, motivated by a desire to destroy or discredit the faith of their fathers. They have simply been moved to apply their Godgiven talents to explore His universe.

And what of today? Never before in human history has man put questions to nature with such energy, sophistication and success. And never before has the area of the unknown shrunk with such rapidity. Science has become a major force and way of life for the twentieth century. In short, we are caught up in an explosion of human knowledge which has led to an unprecedented scientific-technological revolution. This revolution, in turn, is having and will continue to have profound impact on the social, economic, cultural and political realities for our day and for all time. In the context of this symposium, it has also become a period when science and religion are faced with many potential points of conflict and adjustment. Let me identify some of the more difficult areas.

The biological scientist, using primarily the tools of physics and chemistry, comes ever closer to discovering the mechanics of physical life itself. Some of these investigators are motivated primarily by the desire simply to know. Others are more pragmatically concerned with the resolution of the problem of cancer. Since cancer is abnormal growth, they reason that it might well follow that cancer can be understood and dealt with only as one understands the ultimate nuances of normal growth. But, regardless of motivation, it is not beyond the realm of possibility that man may in fact be able to create in the laboratory, from nonliving chemicals, something that has the capacity to live and reproduce itself. The accusation is made that this is tampering with a phenomenon outside the province of man. To this I would comment that man is a great deal more than a physical mechanism, and I know of no scientist who is seriously discussing the question of creating spirit or ethic.

Related to the foregoing is the recent remarkable expansion of knowledge in the field of the chemistry of genetics. It is now possible to identify within the cell itself chemical elements that are precisely related to specific physical characteristics. Here again one hears the accusation that man has no right to tamper with the delicate mechanism which God has provided for perpetuating the image of man. I will admit that this may ultimately pose a serious and profound ethical problem, for if we learn the ultimate details of the mechanics of human heredity, it would then be possible to change and modify the future image of man. The implications both for good and evil in such a possibility are enormous. This should not, I think, frighten us but make even clearer the importance of a vital ethical force in our society. Here religion will be challenged, not to withdraw from the arena, but to enter it boldly so that when man faces the decision as to how to use this knowledge, he will do so in ethical as well as pragmatic and functional terms.

The exploration of outer space is at this moment mainly within the realm of the physical sciences, except as it relates to the capacity of an astronaut to withstand the unusual stresses to which he is subjected in flight. However, beyond the present primitive and tentative probing of space, lies the uneasy and unsettling question of life on other planets. Does it exist and in what form? Ancient, as well as modern, fundamentalist religious philosophy has declared that man is unique and only for this earth. To comment with any certainty with regard to life on other planets is to be dangerously speculative at this moment in history. Yet, we must be prepared to face the ultimate discovery of another living thing perhaps even more advanced than man on earth. Again, I cannot see why one who has a deep and abiding faith in God and His genius and who is not an egocentric should be disturbed about this potentiality. On the contrary, he should be excited at the prospect of still further evidence of the grandeur and power of God in His infinite capacity.

The explosion of knowledge and the speed of modern life have made it increasingly difficult for man to adapt himself to his environment in a state of personal peace and tranquility; hence, the growth of emotional instability and overt psychiatric illness. In these matters man has advanced remarkably since even the last century when mental illness was regarded as irreversible and some kind of supernatural curse. Today we have with wisdom been able to equate mental illness with physical illness and deal with it in the open and with ever greater success. Both from the psychological point of view on the one hand and the neurological-pharmacological approach on the other, great strides have been made in discovering important biological realities and interpreting the capacity of our brain to dream, to think and to conceptualize. These investigations have led to some of the sharpest conflicts between religion and science in that the seat of man's ethical and emotional being lies within the brain, and dealing with these matters has been one of the primary and most jealously guarded responsibilities of organized religion. It is my view that most of these conflicts spring primarily out of what might be called the "jurisdictional" problem. Some of the most gifted psychiatrists I have known, even in the psychoanalytic field, are very religious men, with a fervent belief in God and, in some instances, active and dedicated workers on behalf of the church. The problems in this area are so enormous that what is needed is not division or distrust, but members of the clergy with a friendly familiarity with modern psychiatry, both its possibilities and limitations, and psychiatrists who comprehend and support the great religious requirements of man and society. There is a vast role for both to play in the sense of complementing rather than competing.

Finally, I must take note of what has come to be called the worldwide population explosion. In increasing chorus, scientific and political leadership of the world are pointing to the economic, political and cultural dangers inherent in a continuation of the rapid uncontrolled growth of world population. A few months ago, while in South America, I expressed to one of the leading statesmen of that continent my pleasure at the great postwar industrial development in his country and suggested that this was a happy portent for a higher standard of living and increased political stability in his country. Sadly he responded to the effect that although there had been, in absolute terms, great development of industry and agriculture, the population growth during the same period had been so great that the per capita income of his people had actually fallen.

The application of a whole range of public health techniques in all parts of the world, including sanitary engineering, improvement of nutrition, reduction of insect-borne illness, etc., has led to a remarkable increase in life expectancy, and this process is only just begun. The time-honored Malthusian checks and balances of population no longer obtain due to great scientific breakthroughs. Furthermore, increased communication in our ever shrinking world has led to the realization on the part of hundreds of millions of people that starvation, chronic illness and high infant mortality are not a part of their birthright and can in fact be prevented, and people once informed will not settle for less; hence, actual as well as potential resentment, unrest and resultant political instability.

On the other hand, science has made available to society precise means of controlling population. Is society to be denied the benefit of this knowledge and its application in the name of ethics or are we to continue to expect population to be controlled by such horribly unethical techniques as war, starvation and disease? Here is an issue, of course, fraught with explosive conflict between a large and influential segment of religious belief and the pressing realities of a twentieth-century world caught up in an unprecedented scientific revolution. For myself, I do not believe this matter can any longer be swept under the carpet. Happily, the political leadership in such countries as Japan and India has proceeded to face the matter realistically, candidly and, I believe, in terms of the alternatives, ethically. Let me summarize this issue by simply noting that, in my judgment, there is no situation fraught with greater peril for this and succeeding generations as that relating to the uncontrolled growth of the world's population. We ignore it or refuse to come to grips with it, with the precise technical tools presently at hand, only at enormous and perhaps ultimate peril. Conflict there will be between science and religion in this matter. Being essentially optimistic about man, I believe that reason will again triumph.

I have drawn a few examples from a list of many more to illustrate in the field of biology the impact of our great twentieth-century revolution on established religious belief or practice. At the same time, I would wish to note clearly that although the application of reason is essential to dealing with this revolution and its byproducts, it is all done in a vacuum unless this reason is leavened with ethical principles and ultimate faith in the dignity and destiny of man. Although this is a period in which science would appear in some quarters to reign supreme, a strong case can be made that this is exactly the point in history when a deep and meaningful philosophy of life or religion, as I would prefer to call it, is more essential than ever before if we are to come through.

The power and energy of our day spring from the revolution of knowledge. The navigation and direction of the thrust must come from our belief and our faith. Reason and faith—science and religion—must now more than ever before go hand in hand. The intercommunication between these forces, therefore, must be increased in both directions for one can only enrich and give vitality to the other.

Religion without the acceptance and understanding of scientific investigation and scientific truth is but a dusty museum specimen and will be so regarded by a society that must live with the realities of science. Science without a deep ethical component and lacking faith in God and His infinite wisdom is but a metal skeleton without heart and soul, lacking ethical relevance. Sterile dogmatic and doctrinaire debate between the religionist and the scientist must give way to a joining of the hands on behalf of a society that now must proceed through these revolutionary days by way of reason as well as by way of faith.

There will be many ways of expressing this, for a free society permits—even demands—such public discussion and one is delighted to note an increasing chorus of scientists commenting on the subject. In recent days, the distinguished President of the University of Chicago, Dr. George Beadle, a Nobel prize-winning geneticist, in effect observed that the scientist in a way is the last person who can live without faith in the Deity. He noted that even were the scientist to be able to create life starting with only hydrogen, at that moment, he would then have to ask himself, "But from whence came the hydrogen"?

The late great Jesuit priest and scientist, Pierre Teilhard de Chardin, wrote:

> I feel how much the exploration of the earth in itself fails to bring any light or point out any solution to the most fundamental questions. And I know, too, that the wider the problem seems to grow before my eyes, the more clearly I see that its solution can only be sought in a "faith" beyond all experience.[1]

[1] Pierre Teilhard de Chardin, *Letter from a Traveller*, Harper & Row, New York.

God has given us the curiosity, the brain and the senses, and according to His will and His plan, Man has applied these with enormous success. The quest for knowledge is never over, and areas of the unknown existing today will tomorrow stand exposed by the torch of the scientist. Surely the investigator's reaction will be one of pride in accomplishment, but, at the same time, reverent awe before the revelation of still another of God's miracles.

# DISCUSSION TWO

DR. YINGER: One particularly serious question came to my mind as I heard these two very interesting and challenging papers. It was the question of the ultimate impact of the development of biology and medicine on religion. Let me cite approximate facts. I can't be sure of all these, but I believe these are relatively correct. Two hundred years ago, in even the most highly-developed parts of the world, life expectancy was 20 or 30 years; 250 out of every 1,000 died before the first year of life was finished. By the end of 10 years nearly half were dead. The average couple did not see their 15th wedding anniversary before one of them died. When the second one died at the average age of about 50, he had already witnessed the death of two or three of his children, of whom he had probably had five.

Contrast that with the life of modern urban America, and one must know that biological and medical science has made an enormous impact on (to quote Paul Tillich's idea of religion) "the ultimate concern." "Religion," Tillich said, "is that which concerns man ultimately." Now certainly death is among our ultimate concerns. But new things have been added; and at least the opportunity for the reach of religion has been extended by the development of the biological and medical sciences. We no doubt need to continue our deep concern with the fact of death—I speak here poignantly, having attended the memorial service for the eighteen-year-old son of a very close friend of mine four days ago. This presses in on man; there is no doubt that it will.

There are other things now that religion can afford, in a sense, to struggle with, because of the achievements of biology and medicine—things that could not fully be grappled with earlier, like the tendency to treat one another ignobly, to support and continue those personal habits and social practices that block the full potential of many a human being, or the massive hostility that still exists between groups. The great achievements of biology and medicine offer us the possibility as religious people to push further in our ultimate concerns and thus to extend the reach of our religion.

Dr. Pollard: As I listened to these two very fine, sweeping expressions of the whole range of contribution both to understanding and to man's welfare in the field of the biological and medical sciences, two thoughts occurred to me. One has to do with Dr. White's statement about immortality. Of course it is true that if there is no reality beyond space and time and matter, the only kind of immortality we can have is the kind that Plato and Aristotle, the Hebrew prophets and such people, "the Immortals," now enjoy. But it also struck me that only one person out of perhaps a hundred million human beings can count on any such immortality; as for the rest of us, that kind of immortality is not ours to have. This raises the question as to whether our Creator and Redeemer has, in fact, prepared something more for us—whether there is a way of getting out of the trammels of mortal existence (because we are all mortal, and, whatever biology and medicine do, we'll ultimately die, even if we live to be 150 years old). Death is something we've all got to face and it sharpens, perhaps, this question as to whether there is anything beyond.

Secondly, I think of the common supposition that the supernatural—the area of supernature, of that which transcends space and time—has been radically shrinking as science has advanced. So it has, if the domain of transcendent reality is defined as that simply which we have not yet been able to explain scientifically. But to me, the reality of this domain is in no way dependent on scientific explanation. All Dr. White's examples, I would fully agree, are a mistaken attribution to the supernatural. They are natural phenomena in one sense; but every one of them, too, is inextricably involved, as I see it, with the supernatural. This takes two forms. One can suppose that the whole history of humanity started out with practically everything "supernatural" and very little "natural," in primitive societies and cultures, and that the course of human history is to be seen as the triumphant march of scientific explanation, eliminating the supernatural, and demonstrating that what was previously supposed to be supernatural can now be explained in terms of natural laws and principles. I doubt if the motivation of primitive man was our kind of motivation to explain and control. He was respondng to something very real. His motivations were not to try to understand and control nature so much as to place himself in a relationship with the whole of reality; and I believe this is true even if one examines present-day primitive cultures. They are not motivated as we are—they are partially so, but the role of the supernatural is not just the final sum of magical schemes to explain why things happen the way they do—it is something much more than that. What I'm talking about—a "reality which transcends space and time"—I would apply most particularly to those areas where we have a maximum amount of scientific knowledge, not a minimum. And there I believe reality stands forth as sharply as it ever did.

Mr. WELLS: I'd like to take a comment of Dr. White's and use it as a basis for two questions. The comment was that the search for understanding of the unknown is an obligation of mankind. Although this was Dr. White's statement, I would judge from Dr. Murphy's discussion that he would concur also in this statement. I would like, therefore, to pose these questions either to Dr. White or Dr. Murphy. First, is this not the obligation of all of us, whether we be clergymen, laymen or scientists? Secondly, is the search for understanding or even the attainment of understanding in itself enough? I think Dr. Murphy touched on this last evening. I think I am pretty sure I know what his answer would be; but do we not also have an obligation to relate this better understanding of the unknown as we achieve it—to relate it to our human existence, both material and spiritual?

Dr. WHITE: There is often a great difficulty in applying knowledge—new knowledge. The application comes often very slowly. It should move faster—it is moving faster. For example, much more science writing is good nowadays. Paul de Kruif's book "Microbe Hunters," which I quoted, was one of the very first, very satisfactory (although we thought at the time it was very brief) bits of science writing. I think that it is our obligation to apply the new things that we discover. Certainly we try to do it in medicine, in the biochemistry and biophysical fields which apply to medicine; but it comes very slowly. Nevertheless I accept it as an obligation that we should apply this, not only to the bodily side of men but to the mind and spirit, too.

DR. MURPHY: I would just like to add that I think this is almost the essence of it all. Knowledge I cannot ever accept as beautiful per se; it is beautiful but it ceases being beautiful when it is put in a vacuum or in a museum. Knowledge must, I think, be applied by ethical grounds and directions; and this, I think, is the essence of the problem of our day—the capacity to apply this knowledge so that human suffering and human unhappiness, human starvation and all the rest of it is reduced to a minimum. I am not so naive as to say "eliminated," because these things never really get eliminated. I think, however, that this application is made. And this comes back to the word "relevance" again. This knowledge has relevance; and religion must, therefore, have relevance in its application or relation to the knowledge. This is why religion cannot withdraw from the major issues of our day which are generated by the scientific revolution, be they issues of the control of population or management of population, be they issues of the increased rubbing of shoulders of races and creeds and cultures around the world, be they the distribution of farm surpluses which are required to take care of human starvation around the world. In short, my answer to your question is a resounding YES.

DR. WHITE: May I add a comment? It is said that there is a difference between the science and the art of medicine, and that once it was all art, and gradually science has taken some of the art away. But I would object to the use of the term "art" as applied, for example—well, to the simple bedside manner. The doctor's knowing how to deal with the person, the individual, I think is knowledge, science, not just art.

DR. MOLLEGEN: I found both the addresses so provocative that I have an embarrassment of riches here! Some of the medical knowledge was in struggle with certain types of religion which I wouldn't be seen dead with. And I think that Christianity must be judged by its better—or at least its average—expressions in the twentieth century and not by its worst expressions in the twentieth century, or by its uninformed expressions in the nineteenth, eighteenth, or fourteenth. I think I am a fairly average Anglican, and I am convinced (and I happen to teach moral theology), that while new scientific knowledge creates new and great moral problems, the answer to none of these moral problems is to stop the search for knowledge or to limit its accessibility to people and its application. I would say that that attitude is fairly representative of intelligent Christianity today.

It never crossed my mind to be disturbed in any ultimate sense about the possibility of finding rational life on other planets. Least of all did it ever occur to me as a moral theologian to trust in war, disease, death—premature death —to solve the over-population problem. I am in great demand in the Washington, D.C., area to debate against Roman Catholic moral theologians because it happens that I do not think that the only other way to control this is by sexual abstinence. Nor would it ever occur to me to be deeply disturbed if man were to be able—the biochemists

—to produce living material, or even if he were finally to produce a man. It would only mean to me that he went to school to God's nature, and following God's footsteps learned to do it. Nor would it in any way occur to me to say that God didn't create the result even though He created it through man. If we should create test-tube men, I should probably only want to say I prefer the original way.

It has always been a peculiarity of the Unitarian faith —even those who are only partially related to it—that they have never understood classical Christianity. This is probably in part due to the fact that many Christians do not understand classical Christianity. I find it somewhat paradoxical for nineteenth-century Unitarianism to reject the classical Christian doctrine of the resurrection of the body because it was entirely too psychosomatic, and to prefer the old Platonic and pagan idea of the inherent immortality of the soul; whereas in the twentieth century it rejects the immortality of the soul because it is not psychosomatic enough.

*At this point, it was time to introduce the three "reactors."*

MRS. HECKEDORN: The subject of mortality has been discussed in detail. What I would like to ask is, what is the doctor's Christian responsibility to the patient who faces an incurable disease, if he is to consider man in his wholeness of body, mind and spirit? How can the physician help the man to face the verdict of approaching death?

DR. WHITE: I asked for those questions! It's very difficult —this question of euthanasia—because we all know people we wish could have their lives terminated in some way, perhaps unconscious for a long time or suffering for a long time. Yet this has not been done, and I think at the present time quite rightly, for two particular reasons. Most important from my standpoint is that we can never tell when there's a cure around the corner. It happened when the antibiotics came out. First penicillin. . . . I had some patients with what we called bacterial endocarditis; and we had got so used to their dying with this disease—not rapidly; it often lasted miserably for six months—but death always came in 99.9% of the cases. Then suddenly, while some of them were ill and would have died, and we might have said, "Well, why bother any more in their treatment; why not ease their way out of this life," the antibiotics came in and saved them. George Minot, who got the Nobel price for the discovery of the liver treatment for pernicious anemia, three years earlier had his life saved by insulin. He had diabetes, and he was very ill, and he was one of the first to be treated by insulin, which allowed him to live long enough (and longer after that, too) to make an important discovery himself. These are some of the examples of the possibility of unexpected new discoveries that may help a patient who has been hopelessly ill or hopelessly in pain.

Another, of course less pressing reason, is that it is somewhat of a dangerous tool. It can be used unethically, even criminally, and there may be other reasons—so that euthanasia is still, I think, a matter of question.

DR. POLLARD: If I understand the question correctly, it did not have to do with euthanasia. It had to do with how to minister. What does the doctor say to a person who knows he is doing to die? How do you help a person who confronts his own mortality?

MRS. HECKEDORN: Yes, I am a member of a physician's family, and constantly my husband is coming home with the question, "What can I tell this man who is facing death?" It is a very real question in our household—something I think many doctors would like to know the answer to. Does the priest enter into this or is this the realm of the physician? Can the priest help the physician or help the patient?

DR. POLLARD: I myself have had to help clergymen in such problems, and not only in those problems but in others on which we have worked together. I think it is an individual matter. Some patients who are sick want to know —they must know and they should know. Others don't want to know. It isn't necessary to tell most of the patients who are very ill. They are quite intelligent; they know they are very ill, and they don't necessarily want to be told they are going to die in two weeks; and I think you have to handle this problem individually, according to the temperament and the desire of the individual patient.

DR. MOLLEGEN: A Christian minister, whether he be a layman and a physician or in the priesthood, tries to set death in the context of the ultimate faith. St. Augustine said that the reliance in trust upon the power and love of God revealed in Christ "raised up" your life. In other words, the resurrection of the dead was less difficult to believe than the affirmation, "I believe in God the Father Almighty, Maker of heaven and earth." For the mystery of existence, the being of all things which comes out of nothing, is far more difficult to understand than the raising up of that which has been. Creation itself—the existence of all that is—is the great mystery and the great miracle, and the only reason we don't realize this is because we have become so acclimated to it. We live in it all the time.

DR. WHITE: I would like to add a word about immortality, and that is that it isn't necessary to be a great immortal to utilize one's spirit helpfully. Everybody can do that, with his neighbors, his family, and the people around him. In this way his spirit may aid many. It is not necessary to become a famous "Immortal."

DR. MOLLEGEN: I just commented because I guess it is not even inappropriate that physicians disagree. It has been known. I must say that, although I think that there is a great deal useful in the notion that man has a right to be concerned with the impact of his deeds on this as well as future generations. This is a proper and moral and not evilly egocentric notion. It somehow—again this is perhaps an egocentric comment—but it somehow doesn't jibe with the ultimate beauty of this total phenomenon to believe that the final immortality of most of us is a gene that was once ours ten generations down the road, a biological immortality—the fact that we sort of pass along some chemicals. I have the feeling that my Unitarian friends close their minds—perhaps this the proper, non-Baroque, New England way to look at life and beauty—but I think they tend to close their minds somehow to the ultimate beauty and design. Personally I simply cannot relate to an immortality of simply a memory type on the one hand, or a nucleic acid type on the other, which is the chemical within the genes which passes along.

DR. WHITE: But this example that you can set for others can be very beautiful.

DR. MOLLEGEN: Yes, indeed, I agree—I agree. Touchè.

DR. BARNES: The physician is seeing uncomfortable people all day long every day, and it is his job to attempt to make them comfortable. I use the word "comfortable" rather than "cure" because I have decided that the physicians don't really cure; we treat, and some get better and some don't. We have one of our greatest problems with medical students in teaching them that we actually don't cure, because the physician becomes very uncomfortable when he finds he can't. Even with all of our 2,000 laboratory tests and X-rays and case histories and physical examinations all day long every day, we find that we still don't do very well with a lot of people.

The American Medical Association has recognized this problem, and has taken the initiative in the religious field even before the churches came to us. Last year the delegation from Oregon to the A. M. A. passed a resolution to set up a department of medicine and religion in the American Medical Association. Our director of medical and religious education is in a dilemma because he may come to see local clergymen and say that the doctors here are interested in health and how they believe it can be benefited by coordinating it with religion, but what can the clergyman do? He's asked a lot of them this, and they are very enthusiastic, but nothing has happened. So my question to the panel is "Now that the doctors have made the first step toward coordinating medicine and religion, what has the Church got to offer the doctors?"

DR. MOLLEGEN: One of the most encouraging developments in the modern Church is the increasing number of vocational conferences where representatives of theology and official religion meet with lawyers, doctors, industrialists, elected statesmen, university professors, butchers, bakers, candlestick makers, and what not, and try to find —not by the official representatives of the Church telling them, but in mutual sharing of knowledge and of the situation in which the person, doctor, lawyer, butcher, baker finds himself—the relationship of Christianity to the life of that particular man in his job. These are the most exciting things, I think, that the Church is doing. It happens that physicians are among those who are meeting with us on this. This is one thing that the Church is doing. There is a whole library on Christianity and its relationship to medicine and to the practice of medicine.

DR. POLLARD: I would like to comment on this question of curing people. Both the physician and the priest have this experience of ministering to people's needs. I think a lot of young priests would like to feel that they themselves could have a hand in curing the souls committed to their charge. As they grow older and become wiser, they realize that they only can, as St. Paul says, "plant." Others can water; but it is God who does the curing. My own experience is that a good many wise physicians have this same sense about their ministry to the physical well-being of people—that they plant and water, they do what the best of our knowledge knows to do, but then the patients— the patients and the Lord—take over, and mysterious things happen that wouldn't have happened without the assistance of the physician. But here the physician and the priest and the patient all learn something of the reality of grace, and the reality of that dimension which thrusts itself with power from on high right into the midst of both the "psycho" and the "somatic" in the totality of human existence, and is a living power in the totality of our scientific knowledge. That this reality is there, and to discover that, is the greatest discovery that anyone can make. Because then, even if you don't get well, you have a new kind of confidence about your relationship to the ultimate power of the universe that can't be destroyed by any mortal event in space and time.

Dr. White: I could have agreed wholeheartedly to what has just been said forty years ago, at a time when we were pretty helpless and father was still using sugar pills very effectively. But now even somebody without any milk of human kindness can really cure people. It's nice to have a good spiritual relation with one's patient, but straight cures can be made now both surgically and medically in an infinite number of conditions that were impossible a generation ago. I'm sure that the attitude of the physician, which we call the "art" added to this scientific therapy, is much needed and very helpful. But we can really now have absolute cures of many conditions which were im- possible a generation ago.

Fr. Bigliardi: I was interested in listening to Dr. Murphy, who paints a wonderful picture of the area of the material

that we used to ascribe in our ignorant days to the supernatural, being shrunken down to nothing. I am glad he
also recognized that as this area shrinks to nothing, the
area of the problem increases tremendously; and I daresay
that the first person to recognize that there is no longer
any unknown, is going to have to find some way to say
"My Lord and my God" in the next breath. Ultimately, I
expect that we will discover at this point as in any other,
that Christ is the healer of nations and societies as well as
men.

There are two areas, I think, which trouble me just a
little. I have no particular axe to grind in the matter of
the population explosion, either as to method or to reason.
I have a very great uneasiness, however, that a lot of people
who are concerned here, try to advance the most obvious
solution as the only solution. And so my one question here
would be what other alternatives have been rejected? The
reason I worry so much is that the obvious solution often
leads us into haste, as I am sure we have all recognized
in the tragic circumstances surrounding the drug thalido-
mide, which was used as a way to go to sleep, and ended
up deforming babies.

This brings me to a second area, and that is the limits of
research or at least the responsibility for research. I have
a vague uneasiness about doctors. I think anybody who puts
on a white coat has me at his mercy—I don't know what
to do about it. But yet I have a very great uneasiness about
this because I ask myself whether they do any agonizing
soul-searching in this area, just as the atomic scientists did
when they blew up the first bomb. So my second concern
is whether or not they have asked questions about whether
there are limits to their research, as well as whether (as in

the question of the population explosion) they have not accepted the obvious solution as being the only one.

I would like to mention, third, what Dr. Barnes has said. He asked, "What does the Church have for the doctors?" I would like to ask the reverse, as a person who is deeply and passionately interested in the healing of the sick, because I believe that this is one of the essences of our life in the Church. "What has the doctor to say to the Church?" What sort of a partnership might he like to offer to us? Or would he like us to go away and mind our own business, and stick to trying to comfort people and tell them to be brave?

THE MODERATOR: Well, I think that's really three questions. I am going to ask Dr. Murphy if he wants to respond to the first one.

DR. MURPHY: Well, I'm not sure, as far as the first question is concerned, just to what part of my speech his reference would relate. I think there is no one here this evening, here on this panel, naive enough to believe that scientists now or in the future claim that they will reveal all of the ultimate truth. This is nonsense, of course. It was not even implied. What was stated flatly is that the scientific revolution will proceed apace and the area of the unknown in biological, physical, social terms will shrink. But since the area of the unknown is infinite, it will never shrink to zero. So I simply declare that this question is a non-sequitur, and I think was answered in the body of both statements.

Now the second question, which was a specific one about the explosion of population, is a technical one. Some of the very best scientific brains of our century are trying to deal with it now, and deal responsibly and thoughtfully. Demographers have a whole range of notions about this. There is one clichè that you industrialize society and the birth rate falls off. Perhaps this will come ultimately, a long way down the road. But indications are that at least during a long period of industrialization of society all that happens is that the per capita income falls (but this is really a subject for discussion tomorrow). It's a social scientific matter much more than a theological matter.

I should say parenthetically that one of the problems of our day may be manifest by one aspect of the question. We are coping with such an enormously complex set of factors in dealing with our personal, social and economic problems, that above everything else we must be precise in the public discussions of (a) our facts and, (b) the inferences that flow from these facts. The drug that was used most unfortunately in Germany for the tranquillization of all kinds of people (including those, as is often the case, who require it during the period of pregnancy) had nothing to do—even in terms of motivation of giving it—with the reduction of fertility. It was given to all kinds of people. It just happens that some people who were pregnant got it as well. It was not a drug designed for the control of fertility.

Further, the same kinds of dangers arise in the giving of a whole range of drugs. Drugs have been developed over the past—like all of the antibiotics that most people have taken for one kind of infectious disease or another. The kinds of drugs that are given to people with heart disease and all the other kinds of things today had to be given a first time. Fortunately, out of experience in this country at least, we have a very complex, and, I think, as far as possible, highly-protective system to test these drugs—first on animals, and then very carefully and under carefully-controlled conditions on human beings. So again I make a secondary point by reference to the first point.

Finally, I would just like to say that I don't quite understand the meaning of this phrase, "limits to research." If it means "does the scientist believe that there is an ethical barrier beyond which his investigations should not go; are there things around him that he dare not examine?", I think I am prepared to say, on behalf of most scientists, that they would reject this out of hand. On the other hand, if it means "Are there limits to the ability of scientists?", obviously there are—human limits, limits of technique, limits of tools, and so forth. But had there been limits—ethical limits—to the curiosity of science, human knowledge would have stopped—when? The third century, the fourth century, the fifth century? Investigators have had to push against a whole range of forces in society that have declared ethical boundaries to knowledge for at least as long in history as the last seventeen hundred years.

DR. WHITE: May I take the last question, which was about the coordination of the clergy and the medical profession? This has already been referred to; but I hold in my hand a page from the *New England Journal of Medicine* of June 28 this year, and I will read just a bit of it. It's an editorial entitled "Medicine and Religion."

It must be with a feeling of sympathetic approval that physicians and indeed all sensitively animated persons will react to the creation of a department of medicine and religion within the American Medical Association. Despite a currently propounded theory that the physician should restrict his interest and activities to the healing art alone, and leave all of the matters such as the economics of his profession in more sophisticated hands, the restoration of mind and body has nevertheless generally been a coordinated effort, and rightly so, and this is the purpose of the new department of the American Medical Association, to provide better health for the whole man, according to the Rev. Dr. Paul B. McCleave, its director. It will carry out this purpose by fostering close physician-clergy relations through local medical society programs, by providing counselling service through State, County and local medical societies and by creating leadership teams of physicians and clergymen including psychiatrists and hospital chaplains on the State level. Pilot programs have already been established in nine states from Georgia to Montana, from Texas to New York. This wholesome movement has thus extended to the very borders of New England where according to an academic tradition the stock of the Puritans still survives.

May I just add one last word, and that is—it is encouraging to hear the optimistic attitude of our clergymen. As to the psyche, we believe very ardently in the spirituality that is in the religiosity of man, no matter how you call it.

THE MODERATOR: I think you can recognize that in this discussion we have skirted around the deepest questions of the human spirit. I was moved at points to hope that sometime we would take four nights and talk about the meaning of the word "supernatural." This, I think, would not hurt us at all, because time and again we have been caught up on semantic difficulties which impede and darken thought. So often the word "supernatural" is used simply to mean the mysterious, the ignorant, the whimsical—

something that cannot for the moment at least be assigned to any more intelligent cause, as in insurance policies, when the worst of all possible things is known as "an act of God." Well, this way of talking about God does not commend itself to serious theologians! But we do get involved in this.

We skirted around the area of the supernatural and yet saw that always the heart of many of our practical questions was this far more profound and indeed frightening questions of the real size and dignity of life. Or again, we skirted around the question of interference with life itself. Modern medical science has done so much to increase our capabilities for this kind of interference and it is frightening. In some ways we have always been able to interfere with life. The most radical interference with life that man can perform is to take it away; and that power has never been very far from us. But in our time we can monkey with people in more different ways, and monkey with their children and their unborn grandchildren. This is disturbing; and the question that again comes to mind is, "where are the sanctities which in time past have operated and doubtless will operate, but are not clear at the moment?" What are the ultimate sanctities which in time past have kept us from just promiscuous murder? Where are the sanctities operating now in human society which in time past have made us care that people got well in spite of our ignorance and our follies?

These are the great questions around which we tip-toed tonight, and I don't know that anybody can do any better at this point. It would be folly indeed to wander into the heart of one of these areas merely proclaiming ancient truth. But the sanctities are there to be found, I have no doubt—those great shafts of revelation of the supernatural

God Who little by little helps us to understand the nature which is the curtain and cloak of our spirit. Those are the things we have been thinking about really, and I hope God will lead us through just such thoughtful, troubled, and perplexed exploration of this whole mystery of life and death, and guide us to see what the real questions are and to find answers on which we can build the kind of life of which both Dr. White and Dr. Murphy reminded us so wonderfully and deeply.

# III

# THE SOCIAL SCIENCES

PROF. J. MILTON YINGER
THE REV. A. T. MOLLEGEN

*Discussion "Reactors":*

William Adams II
Miss Louise Bowler
The Rev. Paul Langpaap

# The Social Sciences in the Space Age

### Prof. J. Milton Yinger

NO SOCIAL sciences exist in an isolated or slowly changing society. It is difficult to ask "why do men behave the way they do," if no alternative ways are known to compare and contrast. When social mobility or change disrupt traditional ways of doing things and reveal variation in behavioral standards, men start to wonder about causes. On first experiencing the range of customs and practices, men have been more likely to respond with bewilderment and resentment than with curiosity. How, they may ask, can people behave in such strange and evil ways, so unlike our own proper ways?

Gradually this way of questioning has been changed, at least for a few persons, under the particular impact, of three forces:

1) Centuries of contact across cultural lines háve reduced some sense of strangeness; different ways of doing things begins to be taken for granted.

2) Social change and mobility, because they create new needs and expectations or disturb the accepted patterns of behavior, may seriously disrupt the workings of a society; periodic economic depression, outmoded political institutions, intergroup hostility, or personal demoralization call urgently for attention.

3) If, in this context, science has been invented and applied to those aspects of nature that are most readily quantified and observed, it is likely an attempt to apply the same method to the study of human behavior will take place in an effort better to understand and deal more effectively with the problems being faced.

Extensive development of social science has taken place only in open or democratic societies. This contradicts the idea that knowledge of human behavior has been sought and used mainly by totalitarians attempting to create a "brave new world." Those knowing little of social science uses and areas of its greatest development sometimes associate it with the manipulations of a threatened "1984." But, totalitarian societies have repressed all but its most technical and fact gathering aspects. Knowledge of the roots of human behavior, the range of values and opinions among human beings seem relatively useless to those who believe they know exactly what society's goals should be and who hold rigidly an ideology that gives them presumed knowledge of how to proceed.

I

Before I turn to a brief discussion of the diverse problems of contemporary social sciences, and a look into the future, their shared perspective should be noted. Despite diversity, the disciplines of anthropology, demography, economics, history, political science, psychology, social psychology, and sociology share a great deal in common. All are concerned with some aspect of the question: How is it that man behaves and has behaved under various conditions? What are the basic forces at work? How can we extend the objectivity, the precision, and the scope of our observations? How can we achieve *controlled* observation (in the scientific sense of the term), so that the combined effects of multiple forces, which offset or augment each other in various ways, can be sorted out?

These are old questions. And the funded answers accumulated through the centuries are rich in "common sense" upon which contemporary observation draws. But common sense is a woefully inadequate guide in a rapidly changing society. Without taking time to document this assertion, let me simply say common sense is often false; it leaves many gaps; it contains mutually contradictory propositions; and, most importantly, it fails to specify the conditions under which various statements are true. Thus "you can't teach an old dog new tricks," but "never too late to learn" are incipient—and contradictory—theories of education; but they are scarcely of great value. More prosaically, but more helpfully, we ask: Under what conditions are new lessons possible for "old dogs," human or otherwise?

In efforts to extend the reach of controlled observation, social scientists assume that human behavior is subject to natural law, that man is part of nature, that a given cause will be followed by a given effect, other things being equal. Properly understood, this statement is not, I believe, particularly controversial, although many persons are made uncomfortable by it.

It is not an assertion of final truth, but an *assumption* that is useful for certain purposes. The scientist says, in effect: "I am going to assume that human behavior is subject to law, as is the movement of the stars, or the growth of a plant, or the process of atomic fission, or the accumulation of fatty tissue on the inner walls of arteries. On the basis of that assumption, I will attempt, by controlled observation, to determine the sequence of events—when inflation will occur, or prejudice will be learned, or political participation will be extensive—and will try to formulate theories that will aid prediction by specifying conditions under which these various events will occur."

The scientist does not believe his perspective exhausts the meaning of things. He invites others, proceeding from different assumptions, to join him in the exciting effort to understand the world. He only affirms that as a scientist he has to act scientifically, by studying nature in all of its complicated variations.

Science is no substitute for man's evaluing activities. To describe what is taking place is not to declare what ought to take place. Those who look to science, instead of to religion and ethics, for their basic value premises will look in vain. Physical science can show us how to make an atomic bomb, but not whether we ought to make one. Biological science can help to prolong life; but it makes little contribution to the host of new moral and policy questions that press in as a result of that prolongation—the loneliness of the aged, for example, or the problem of their place in the economy. Social science may tell us that under certain conditions a given monetary policy will tend to promote a stable dollar with high unemployment while another policy will promote an unstable dollar with little unemployment; but it cannot say which of these alternatives is better.

I would like to qualify this statement concerning the relationship of science and values in two ways: To say that religion and ethics are the source of values is not to imply that a static tradition is an adequate guide. It is not enough simply to turn to the past since each generation faces new situations demanding thoughtful, contemporary moral and religious thinking. What is required of you and me to be moral in our actions related to the Chinese peasant in 1962? We cannot know without careful study of the world situation and an attempt to understand the consequences of our various possible actions. What problems of values and morality are raised by the fact that the world's population will probably double by the end of the twentieth century, from three to six billions of people? Almost beyond doubt there will be more hungry people in the world at the end of this century than there are now. There will also be more guns, more restless people, more aggressive social movements.

Our great religious and moral traditions can start us on the process of dealing with such value questions, but each generation must interpret and extend these traditions. They are meaningful parts of experience only if we enter into them, actively rethinking them and applying them to our own lives.

This leads to the second qualification I would like to make concerning the relationship of science to values. Although science cannot be the source of our first premise, our ultimate values, it can be of enormous significance by helping to show which goals are possible and what the by-products of various choices may be. Economists and sociologists, for example, cannot rightfully say that America should or should not rapidly extend the automation of its industrial machinery. But they can say: if automation proceeds rapidly, these are some of the consequences for employment, for production, or for the distribution of wealth.

Insofar as they give us firm knowledge, they contribute

greatly to our moral decisions by helping us to understand the results of various policy decisions. In a sense, then, science becomes one of the sources of our second and third level values, if not of our primary values, by saying to the members of a society: If this is the primary goal you want, then you *should* also adopt these other goals, because they are necessary parts of a process. How often in life we proclaim our fervent desire for some goal (world peace, for example), but then proceed—either out of lack of knowledge or out of unwillingness to take the necessary steps, often involving sacrifices—to deny the goal. Science, by describing the steps necessary to achieve various goals and consequences of our actions, can make a major contribution to the value choices.

This relationship description of science to values applies equally to physical, biological, and social sciences. Other questions arise with reference to the social sciences alone, or apply more particularly to them. Many of these questions relate to methodology. Only a small proportion of the work of social scientists takes place in the artificial environment of the laboratory, where the researcher can control and manipulate all the variables that might affect the process he is studying. The laboratory work in social science tends, with few notable exceptions, to be concerned with relatively minor questions.

Commonly we study human beings behaving in their natural settings and then attempt, by comparing two settings that are alike in all important respects but one, to isolate the influence of that one factor. We might ask, for example: Does personal maladjustment cause a boy to become a delinquent?

We cannot study this in a laboratory; we cannot take a

group of babies and attempt to create maladjustment in them in order to compare them later with a matched group, after all have been placed in the same social situation. What we can do is to take a group of delinquents—unhappily created for us—and compare them carefully with a group of non-delinquents. We can select from these two groups persons who are alike in intelligence, racial and national background, extent of schooling, income of parents, number of brothers and sisters—to mention only a few variables—and then see whether the delinquent group has a significantly higher rate of personal maladjustment than the non-delinquent group with whom it has been matched. (This is, incidentally, an exceedingly complicated research problem—probably no less complicated than discovering the cause of cancer. We have, as yet, no definitive answer to the question of the cause of delinquency, although I believe we are getting somewhere near to one.)

This method of research—we can call it the survey method, in contrast to the laboratory method—is clearly less efficient in some ways than laboratory work. It has the advantage of being closer to the nature we seek to understand, but the disadvantage that the scientist himself does not control the sequence of events and therefore cannot be sure that hidden variables are not affecting the result. Some persons have concluded that the relative lack of laboratory research in the study of human behavior is so important that such study ought not to be called science. I see no reason to argue over this question. If you prefer to use the word science as a synonym for laboratory research, then social studies are at most rudimentary sciences.

I know of no economists who can manipulate the decisions of the Federal Reserve Board under controlled conditions in order to study the effects of changes of its rediscount rate; nor do I know of anthropologists who control the lives of people in tribal villages in order to study systematically the impact of modern agriculture on some and the withholding of modern knowledge on others. Changes in rediscount rate do take place, however, and variations in contact with modern agriculture are frequently found. Careful observation can reveal the conditions that were similar and those that were different—pointing the way to causes. This is precisely the logic of all science.

If, therefore, you prefer to use the word science as a synonym for the logic of observation by controlled variation, then many studies of human behavior are properly called science. This, as you might guess, is my inclination. Sciences vary in their specific research processes, their "tactics," as James Conant calls them; but they are alike in basic logical processes, their "strategies." In my judgment, space age social science will not become notably more involved in laboratory research. What will take place is extensive improvement in the precision and representativeness of our data and a great increase in the processing of data by electronic machines. Because of the large number of variables with which it has to deal, social science, even more than physical and biological science, will profit by the use of computers. This is not true at the moment because we do not have enough valid data to make elaborate statistical and mathematical operations meaningful, except in a few instances. The desk calculator, fairly simply statistical procedures, and IBM sorters, of course, are now routine.

Incidentally, if the presence of extensive laboratory research is believed to be the central criterion for science, the disciplines of geology, meteorology, and even astronomy will have to be excluded from the term. Astronomy, of course has become the most precise of the sciences, despite the lack of a laboratory, because it deals with relatively few, highly stable variables that can be expressed in mathematical terms. Thus prediction of astronomical events can be made with great precision.

The social sciences are near the opposite end of the scale, since they deal with many variables which we have not yet learned how to express in precise quantitative terms; hence their predictions are in terms of ranges of probability. It is a mistake, I believe, to forget these methodological differences among the sciences; but it is also a mistake to exaggerate them to the degree that one forgets that there are many ways in which to achieve controlled observation of the natural world.

In addition to this methodological question, there are other aspects of the perspective of social science that I can take time only to mention. These will, I believe, become more and more important. From the beginning of their work, social scientists have had an interest in comparative study. Because of the nature of the data with which they work, this has been essential, both methodologically and substantively. Hydrochloric acid or disease producing viruses behave the same way in the Soviet Union as in the United States; but there are some differences among the human beings in the two lands. This is all too obvious, and yet a consistent comparative approach has been slow to develop.

It has been easier to study persons and groups close at hand; support for the social scientist and his own interests tended to focus his attention on the local or national scene.

The values, motives, and interests of those abroad were then assumed by many to be like those at home. Nineteenth-century economists, and some contemporary ones too, I fear, could not imagine that the economic motives of Western Europeans and Americans were not world-wide constants. Freud tended to develop his theory of personality on the basis of his studies of neurotic, upper-middle class, Viennese women in 1900—to put the issue in an exaggerated form. Oppositely, however, there has been a tendency to assume that the values, motives, and interests of those in other societies were so different as to be inexplicable by the same principles. They are "prelogical," as Levy-Bruhl said of preliterates, because they did not start from the same premises as a well-educated Frenchman; or they are a puzzle, surrounded by mystery, wrapped in an enigma, as Churchill said of the Russians.

In recent years, a consistent comparative approach in all of the social sciences is helping us to avoid these opposite errors. A strong interest has developed, promoted by the vast increase in communication and contact across national lines, in describing variations in values, institutions and behavior. At the same time there are vigorous efforts to discover the universal elements in values and experience. We have finally come to the point, I believe, where the range of variation in human institutions and behavior along with the nature and extent of their universal qualities have become matters for careful research—important empirical questions requiring scientific study—instead of easy assumptions that have blocked our understanding. This makes the work of social science more difficult, but promises also to make it much more fruitful.

Another shift in perspective must be mentioned if we

are to understand present and future developments among the social sciences. A great deal of attention is directed to the understanding of the latent or less obvious functions and consequences of the forces influencing human behavior, along with attention to the more obvious or manifest functions and consequences. The study of latent processes reveals that the human world is more complicated than it seems and emphasizes the need for avoiding interpretations based on the superficial appearances of things.

Perhaps I can illustrate this development by asking a few questions: Is it possible that the Black Muslim religious movement among lower class, urban Negroes in the United States is to be understood, not simply as an attack on the white-man and the society he dominates, but also as an effort to overcome a deep inferiority complex and to acquire the disciplines and skills necessary to greater success in that very society? If so, its latent consequences—greater skill, thrift, self-confidence and discipline among Negroes —are very different from its manifest content, where violence and separation are emphasized.

In a different field we might ask: What are *all* the consequences of the extensive automation of American industry? Before we are very far along in answering that question we will surely note its impact, not simply on productivity, on the sharp reduction in need for unskilled labor, on the ratio of capital to labor expenses, and other technical economic questions, but also on schools (curricula will have to change), on the distribution of power within industry (small units may lose out rapidly), on our class system (with the reduction in need for those of low skill, they will either become a frustrated and unhappy group—

as many are now in this day of high unemployment—or will be absorbed into the middle class).

In the field of political movements one might ask: Is the extreme right-wing in the United States today to be explained on the basis of its most obvious feature: these are people who are more worried about the strength of communism than others? Or is their anti-communism, particularly that aspect of it expressed in suspicion of neighbors or public figures, an effort to struggle with their own insecurities? Insecurities, based perhaps on the fact that they have only recently climbed in status and income and are not certain that they can or deserve to hold on to their newly-won affluence? The latent function of their anti-communism then would be to declare: "See, I surely deserve all that I have won, for I am more patriotic than almost anybody else."

These are, of course, extremely complicated questions. I raise them only to suggest to you the persistent effort being made by contemporary social science to discover those processes in human behavior that lie hidden beneath more obvious features.

II

Having made reference to some aspects of the perspective of social science, let me turn now to a quick survey of some of the central research problems. This list will reflect my own interest, bias, and ignorance, but will contain, I believe, many fundamental questions for the next several decades. I will state them in general terms, not in the form of specific hypotheses, because there are dozens of hypotheses being explored within the context of each of the questions. Nor will any effort be made to identify a problem with a particular social science.

To some degree, identification will be clear because of the nature of the topic; in other instances, several disciplines are undertaking to explore a subject, separately or jointly. This will be no "Buck Rogers'" list, for these questions emerge naturally out of current research interests. Small likelihood exists for a major scientific breakthrough because social sciences deal with situations where so many variables are involved that no one relationship is likely to prove decisive.

Much social science work is still at the level of "natural history," in the sense in which that term is used in botany and zoology. What is the range of individual and group facts, carefully described? How do persons within and between societies vary in religious belief and practice? To what degree do societies differ in their emphasized values? What various familial, governmental, educational, and economic structures are found? Until we have full information on such descriptive questions, more analytic research aimed at discovery of conditions under which various events occur is weakened.

A most important question underlies several others: How is the human infant—so helpless, so lacking in biologically-determined answers to the problems he faces, yet so capable of learning—shaped by the forces within him and surrounding him? What processes lead to creativity, to full use of one's powers, to high achievement motivation, and to lack of inner conflict—or to the opposite of these things? We are getting tentative answers to these vital questions. Perhaps by the end of the century they will be answered with more confidence.

Whenever dramatic population changes occur, interest in demography—the study of the composition and location of the population—is increased. Today intensive efforts are made to study trends and possible consequences of changes in world population. It is now well known that fifty million people are being added to the world's population every year; that many nations have to run very hard to stand still —in terms of food and other resources available *per capita;* that, in general, it is the poorest countries that are growing most rapidly. It is difficult to exaggerate the significance of these trends. Doubtless by Century 21 we will have learned how to chart population facts as precisely as we now chart the rainfall in the watershed of a storage dam or the corn yield in years of plenty or scarcity. Insofar as we have reliable information about population facts, we need not be the helpless victims of their potentially crushing impact.

What is the full significance of the fact that the world is on what is probably a one-way street leading to urbanism? For the first time in human history we have substantially urban societies, with the majority of people living in cities and all people strongly influenced by the urban-industrial complex. Every aspect of life is affected by this development. One could scarcely begin a study of personality formation, economic production, politics, religious trends, recreation, education, social stratification, race relations, the uses of leisure time, or crime—to mention several basic questions—without careful analysis of the influence of the rapid development of urban civilizations.

But what we now know about city life is only a tiny fraction of what we need to know. We are slowly getting rid of the presupposition that urban life is somehow pathological or unnatural. Perhaps as a result we are in a position to ask more meaningful questions about the effects of cities. Obviously many older patterns of life and values are being destroyed. What new ones are appearing? Is mental illness more common in urban societies? The evidence today is inconclusive. Is a heavy crime rate the result of urbanism or of urbanization? What forces give unity to a mobile, heterogeneous, changing, urban society? Such questions command our most intensive study.

When the study of government moves beyond description, the basic question becomes: What are the conditions under which various political events occur? Does the formal structure of government, for example, determine political behavior; or does the whole social context in which politics occurs create the observed structures of government; or is there interaction. This is a question of great practical as well as scientific interest.

Recently, for example, the Supreme Court ruled that certain state practices permitting individual citizens unequal power in choice of representatives were unconstitutional. In some states a rural voter has several times as much power as a city voter. Now those who hold that political structure is a *cause* of political decisions and of other social processes believe that changes produced by the Supreme Court decision will deeply affect governmental actions, especially those initiated in the United States Congress. On the other hand, those who hold that the social context is more important contend that a Court decision, because it does not affect the location of economic power, the stratification system, or the values and motives of the electorate, cannot strongly affect governmental actions, except perhaps temporarily. We scarcely have the setting for a controlled experiment, but we can learn a great deal by observing this situation carefully over the next several years. The lesson it teaches can be critically important to the study of the growth of international governmental structures.

After World War II a growing interest in the study of conflict arose among social scientists. Actually, investigation of self-conflict (inner tensions), race and class conflict, and international conflict is of ancient origin; but systematic empirical study by methods of science has only begun. Indeed, even today, the number of trained investigators working on crucial questions in this area is probably only a small fraction of the number attempting, for example, to discover new synthetic fibres.

A society says a great deal about its values by the way in which it assigns skilled manpower to the solution of its various problems. One might say, perhaps, that Century 21 will never arrive unless we turn our attention to this question with great speed. If social science can give us firm knowledge concerning the roots of conflict it can furnish important—but by no means complete—resources for struggling with the problem.

A most intensively studied economic question at this time relates to causes of economic fluctuation. What governs rates of employment, investment, and productivity? How do psychological, political, and technological facts affect the economic process? What conditions produce sustained economic growth, unimpaired by recessions and depressions? In all technologically developed countries, social scientists keep continuous watch over numerous indicators of economic strength and weakness (very much as meteorologists study indicators of weather change), and recommend appropriate adjustments at various levels of individual, corporate, and governmental policy making.

Predictions of economists are probably of about the same order of accuracy as the weather-man's: both our picnics and our economic booms are sometimes dampened by unexpected drops. But the successes of both exceed their failures by a wide margin; we have been able to prevent wide-scale damage by knowledge of a coming climatic or economic hurricane. And we have one advantage in the economic realm still unavailable to the meteorologist: by foreknowledge we can take steps that prevent some of the unwanted events from occurring. It is surely significant that since the '30's, although we have had several recessions, we have avoided a major depression.

A recent research area of great interest and value has begun to command attention of several social sciences and is likely to be of increasing interest. Anthropology, economics, sociology, and political science share a concern for this question: What are the processes by which technologically underdeveloped societies create self-sustaining economic growth? Is such growth possible, in the contemporary world, without outside resources? Are there stages through which a society must pass (first improving its agriculture, then expanding the level of literacy, then developing a group of trained administrators, for example) in the process of growth?

It is often said that the leaders of new nations are more interested in the symbols of modernization than in the substance of it: They want a steel plant, a generator for electricity, a few jet planes, and some concrete highways as proof of their development even though these items may actually be barriers to economic advance. Is it true that these resources are those often desired first? If so, how does one account for such activity?

First efforts to study the process of change from a position of static-equilibrium to one of continuing economic growth were usually concerned almost entirely with economic questions. Some writers posited a theory of a geometric curve in the sequence of development; but few situations fit this model. Closer to the facts was Rostow's idea of a "take-off" from a flat plateau of economic activity —a theory that took account of the rather sharp discontinuities in economic development. Yet even this interpretation frequently fails to fit the facts.

If one studies the process of development from the point of view of a purely economic model (and a model derived from a Western European and American setting at that) he is likely to make several *assumptions* about human behavior that are not accurate. It proved easy, for example, for American economists to assume that profit maximization is a universal motive, that workers will work harder and longer when their wages are increased, that technological change requires no attention to family patterns, religious values, or traditional perspectives. Viewed from economic considerations alone, technological advance has run into surprising and unexpected resistance.

Some economists have begun to wonder whether anthropologists and sociologists might help them understand why. We are beginning to study societies as social *systems*, more or less integrated structures, not mere collections of separate economic, political, religious, and other institutions and patterns. Technological development threatens the existing power distribution in some societies. It may disrupt the family pattern; (how're you going to keep them down on the farm, once they've seen Paree is matched by the problem of keeping the wife meek and subservient once she has a separate pay check as a worker in a textile plant).

Industrialization may demand behavior that is thought to be of low or degrading value by the elite of some societies, who, at the same time, are the only ones with sufficient training to carry it out. Cultural values may, on the other hand, make industrial development easier, rather than harder, than one would predict from a purely economic model. To predict how rapidly a society can create capital from internal sources requires knowledge of its style of life and values. *We* might not be able to save if we had the income of the Burmese, but the Burmese can when motivated to do so.

In this listing of some of the basic social scientific questions that seem likely to be of central importance in the years ahead, let me mention one other that is of special interest in this series of lectures. If we want to understand society and the behavior of individuals therein, we must surely concern ourselves with religion. Every one of the social sciences must at some point inquire: What are the religious values and organizations among the people I am studying, and how are they involved in their interaction? For some kinds of problems religion can be treated as the dependent variable.

One may inquire, for example, how religious beliefs and practices are affected by the rapid growth of cities, by the developments of science, by war, by the distribution of privilege and disprivilege in a society. If one assumes that religion moves along in splendid isolation from these mundane affairs, he has not studied carefully, for example, the enormous impact of the rapid growth of suburbs or the variation in religious life among the members of different classes and races. On the other hand, the social scientist often finds it necessary to view religion as the independent variable.

Comparative study of technological development must cover the ways in which differences in religious values affect economic growth. No analysis of population trends, political processes, or educational developments would be adequate without attention to the ways in which religious forces are involved.

I will come back to this topic in order to comment on the prospects for religion in the generations ahead, as they appear to the social scientist.

## III

The list of research areas that I have given you can only illustrate the kinds of questions that now command the attention of social scientists and seem likely to be of greatest interest in the early decades of the space age. As work proceeds along these lines, what general trends are we likely to see? Three developments seem to me to be most likely:

1. A great increase in the support given to the social sciences and in the number of persons professionally employed in them.
2. Extensive growth in interdisciplinary work.
3. Applied branches will develop tremendously beyond their present level. Each of these possibilities deserves some comment.

1—My prediction of a great increase in support given to the social sciences is based simply on an extension of present trends, because I see no likelihood of a diminution in the forces supporting those trends. The vast increase of both our productivity and our power for destruction drives us on, by both hope and anxiety, toward the goal of trying to understand ourselves as we are beginning to understand the physical world. Membership in professional societies among social scientists has doubled since World War II. Perhaps a quarter of a billion dollars is spent annually in the United States for social science research, an increase of several hundred per cent in the last generation. (It should be noted, however, that over half of this amount is spent by private business and industrial organizations for attitude and market studies that contribute little to the growth of general knowledge.)

Perhaps most significant is the gradual shift of opinion among physical and biological scientists and among governmental leaders toward the view that substantial support for the social sciences is desirable. When the National Science Foundation was established, shortly after World War II, the social sciences were only minimally and marginally included. Gradually their role in the work of the Foundation has increased. More generally, in April, 1962, a report was issued from the White House, prepared for the President's Science Advisory Committee, which recommends a major increase in support for social scientific research. Support from universities and private foundations is also expanding rapidly. All of this may please you or may dismay you; but it seems likely that social science will occupy an increasingly important place in the life of the Space Age.

2—The second development will be in the direction of more interdisciplinary work. The division of labor among scientists is partly accidental and temporary—the result of the level of knowledge at a given time and the traditional structure of universities. As knowledge grows, as new problems appear, dividing lines become barriers that must be broken. Some of the most exciting work in science today requires the combined perspectives of biology, chemistry, and physics. A man narrowly trained in one of these areas is simply unable to raise many questions related to cell structure, change, and growth. The same kind of situation prevails among the social sciences: many of the most important areas of research demand the perspectives of several disciplines. I have already mentioned this in connection with the study of underdeveloped societies and might add many other illustrations: research on prejudice requires the combined efforts of psychologists and sociologists; old-fashioned political-economy is becoming new-fashioned, as economists and political scientists join efforts; psychiatrists and anthropologists have joined in fruitful collaboration in the study of personality formation; and it is becoming abundantly clear that the understanding of crime requires the cooperation of sociologists, psychiatrists, psychologists, and political scientists.

3—Finally, we shall see in the years ahead a great increase in applied social science. Again, this is a simple projection of present trends. It would have been difficult, fifteen years ago, to imagine the speed with which applied social science has developed. To be sure, there were many clinical psychologists, social workers, governmental consultants, and a scattering of social scientists in business and labor unions; but the great majority were connected with the teaching and pure research of our colleges and universities. During World War II, however, the nation reached for every resource it had. More extensive use was made of social science than ever before, and since then the rate of growth of the applied fields has accelerated.

The President has a council of economic advisors. The UN, UNESCO, and many technical assistance programs employ social scientists. A small but potentially useful social scientific adjunct works with the medical profession with reference to both physical and mental illness. We are discovering that illness is in part a result of disturbed interpersonal relations, that it is affected by cultural values and practices, and that the social organization of medical activities is involved in the process of cure.

Under the somewhat improbable title of "social psychiatry" social scientists are contributing to our knowledge of the causes and treatment of personality disorder. Clinical psychologists and social workers—most of them with social scientific training—are employed before their sheepskins are unrolled. Many cities and states have human relations commissions, applying knowledge of human behavior to the tensions of their communities. Industrial psychologists and industrial sociologists are employed to advise many corporations; and some of their colleagues sit across the table advising the unions. If you want to find out how many Iowa farmers attended the World's Fair last week, a research agency will find out for you—at a price. Students of our inner fears (or our inner ears) sit in the advertising councils (or establish their own agencies) the better to sell the products of American mass production. Even the anthropologists—surely the least likely to be thought of as applied workers—have a Society of Applied Anthropology.

This growth of the applied fields is doubtless inevitable and, in my judgment, desirable. It is not, however, without its difficulties and dangers. These stem in part from the fact that social scientists don't yet know enough; and in part from the fact that, in a sense, they know too much. The advice given by young sciences is not always good, for there are unintended and unexpected consequences. Our clients may come to expect far more than we can deliver and then feel disillusioned when the actual outcome is known.

Charlatans are sometimes able to take advantage of the amorphous nature of the applied professions to sell their fake expertness. And, perhaps most unhappily, when young sciences turn too early to the tasks of technicians and clinicians, their freedom of choice in research and theoretical matters may be limited and their imaginations circumscribed, as the practical problems of their clients, rather than the long-run demands of scientific growth, dictate their work. This need not be so true of more advanced sciences, because society is likely to recognize more fully their contributions by sponsoring pure research alongside the practical applications. The social sciences may face, in the decades ahead, this dilemma: at the very time they can least afford to have pure research slow down, because so much is not yet known, they are pulled into applied fields to prove their worth. We must be on our guard, in the years ahead, to see that the necessary development of applied social science does not lead us to use tentative knowledge too quickly.

I have suggested an opposite difficulty as well. We may come to know "too much." With the growth of knowledge on human behavior, possibilities of manipulation may increase. In 1945, many physicists were brought up short by realization that their discoveries in the field of atomic fission gave mankind a weapon of unprecedented destructive power. They were suddenly confronted with serious moral dilemmas. This same kind of problem is beginning to worry some social scientists. Perhaps industrial psychology and sociology are only aiding the managements of large corporations to manipulate their workers more skillfully. Perhaps knowledge of public opinion formation, through the use of the mass media of communication, will make our elections into battles of wits between public relations firms, with the voter a pawn in the struggles on the airways. If you let this nightmare go on, you see issues disappearing completely from elections, even personalities becoming unimportant, as both parties pick candidates who are vague Rorschach inkblots, with a sweet smile, into whom every voter can read his own predilections.

Now all of this seems to me to be highly unlikely in an open society, where social scientific knowledge is competitively available. We must beware the easy leap from knowledge that a skillful campaign can switch the allegiance of many persons from one toothpaste to another to the assumption that the same procedures can make them switch from one system of basic values to another. All we know about personality and group structure argues against this. And yet it seems, in principle, that as social scientific knowledge grows, we shall be faced with the same moral dilemmas concerning its use now confronting us as a result of the growth of the physical and biological sciences.

## IV

We are led back, then, in conclusion to one of the points with which we started: science is no substitute for mankind's moral and religious quest, although it vitally affects that quest. Because it changes so much of the world within which we live, science requires us to continually rethink our moral and religious heritage. Every religion carries within its traditions limited and partial elements reflecting the times and places of its development. Scientific study of religion leads to the conclusion that religion—some religion— is a universal characteristic of human life, found in all societies.

It also leads to the conclusion that particular religions die out, or are destroyed by a competitor, partly because they become rigid. They may become so fully accommodated to the society of which they are a part—accommodated to its injustices as well as its strengths—that they deal only inadequately with new situations produced by dramatic social changes. Thus many American churches are not yet at home in the city, and are scarcely relevant to many of the central problems of city life; vital changes in our patterns of race relations are being carried out with relatively little participation and guidance by our churches; and the overwhelmingly significant developments in the meaning of nationhood in an era when the world has abruptly become one communication and transportation network are given scant attention by what we somewhat inaccurately call the "world religions."

To be of continuing vitality in the dramatically new societies, partly created by science, religion must participate fully in the process of finding meaning and building new structures appropriate to the contemporary world. The social sciences, by furnishing an accurate picture of the nature of that world can be religion's ally, but they cannot be a substitute for nor an adjunct to religion. Some seek to make social sciences into religion. (And strangely enough, such persons are found not only among the scientists, but also among theologians, some of whom would redefine the assumptions and purposes of social science in such a way as to bring them within the theological world view.) But this would only weaken both endeavors. It is the task of science to broaden our understanding of nature.

Religion, however, is not primarily a search for knowledge but a mode of action—a way of dealing with the ultimate facts of the human condition. The growth of knowledge, therefore, does not diminish the need for religion, although it may change the terms in which it is expressed. Myths and symbols and rituals change, but everywhere man lives by a series of mighty "overbeliefs" that give direction to his endeavor. Each generation is most effectively religious, in my judgment, when its overbeliefs are fully congruent with the best of the intellectual, moral, and aesthetic expressions of its time.

The tension between science and religion can be expressed in the form of constructive challenges, rather than as conflict—a challenge to religion to try to achieve a more adequate view of nature, and a challenge to science to achieve a fuller grasp of the full range of the human condition. By performing their separate but harmonious tasks, science and religion can contribute to the quality of our response to life in the space age.

# The Christian Ethos
# of Empirical Science

## The Rev. A. T. Mollegen

CHRISTIAN theology and Christian social ethics, as I
understand these two disciplines, have no quarrel
with Dr. Yinger's paper. In particular, I should like to concur heartily with his statement, "Science, of course, is no
substitute for man's evaluating activities. To describe what
is taking place is not to declare what ought to take place.
Those who look to science, instead of to religion and
ethics, for their basic value premises will look in vain."

For instance, if I step on your toes, you will know it; I
may or may not know it and observers, scientific or otherwise, will know it. My standing on your toes is a fact of
physics, of biology, of sociology, of history. It is also a fact
for theological and moral understanding and action. This
fact can be described in terms of Newton's laws of motion,
Einstein's theory of relativity, Dr. White's (or any physician's) medical knowledge and Dr. Yinger's (or any social
scientist's) sociology.

Whether it is right for me to step on your toes depends
for a Christian upon his understanding of God, man, love
and justice on the one hand and upon the whole historical

context of the fact on the other hand. For the Christian, you are a human creature of God for whom Christ died and the Christian is one who, in response to God's love in Christ, is gladly and voluntarily obligated to love you as Christ loves you. Being a Christian, however, does not tell me directly whether to step on your toes or not. It does not even tell me that I *am* stepping on your toes. You or an observer may tell me that fact. (*You* are the more likely candidate for the task of informing me.)

Once you and I and the observer are aware of the fact, the problem of evaluating the fact and of acting on the basis of the evaluation of the fact arises. This evaluation depends not only upon my doctrine of God, man, love and justice but upon my understanding of the whole context of the fact. For instance, if I step on your toes inadvertently in the maze at the entrance to the Space Needle, and you yell in protest, I shall get off your toes and apologize. But if I step on your toes as an inevitable part of snatching a child from beneath the descending Bubbleator, my act will be approved as right by you and me, by the child and his parents, and by most of humanity.

One further observation about your toes should be made. From the standpoint of Christianity, and incidentally of the United States Constitution, your toes are inviolable, They are parts of your person. I should not ever step on your toes. It may happen inadvertently or it may happen as the lesser of evils but it is something that should be regretted always. If it is the lesser of evils, then the whole situation should be not only regretted but *repented*.

Now let us substitute for the simple fact of my stepping on your toes, some complex social facts: The fact that six hundred thousand persons sleep upon the streets of Bombay every night, that so far we have reduced unemployment in the United States only to about four million, that we are spending over $50,000,000 a year for military power. If we start with any of these facts, we are forced to see them in a total world context. Could there be any greater argument for the role of the social scientist in the modern world? Social science illumines the world for us by giving us facts and increasing enlightenment as to the relationship of the facts. It is no substitute for Christianity, for morality, for statesmanship, or for responsible citizenship, but it is indispensable to an informed Christian action, an informed statesmanship and an informed responsible citizenship.

This indispensability of the social sciences is comparable to the indispensability of the other sciences. Biology made it possible for man to conquer the so-called bubonic plague which once decimated Europe's population by one-half or two-thirds. Increasing economic knowledge and the assumption of responsibility for a healthy economy by our democratic state has so far averted economic catastrophes of the gravity of that which began for us in 1929.

Christianity has a moral mandate that drives man toward knowledge of everything that affects God's beloved creatures, human and sub-human. This is the Christian *Moral* mandate to know and is especially clear in regard to medical and social sciences. There is, however, an even deeper Christian motivation to know than that of serving our fellow creatures. For Christians knowing is intrinsic to loving. In the Biblical languages, Hebrew, Aramaic and Common Greek, and in the languages influenced by Biblical religion, "to know" is used of the most intimate of personal relationships, sexual intercourse. "Adam knew Eve and she conceived." Knowing is union with the known, it is an action of fellowship. For the Christian, then, to know is a mode of union between God's creatures in the unity of God's great Creation. In the Spacearium here, we see and hear of new creatures of God to know in love. As Christians once naively knew and loved the stars, as Plato once saw in the heavens and their order an approximation and reflection of the symmetry and beauty of the eternal realm, so the modern Christian astronomer may seek knowledge of the galaxies and outer space not primarily because that knowledge is or may be useful but simply because it is knowledge, a mode of loving God's creatures and our fellow creatures.

So also the artist's grasp of his object and his "work" which unveils the object's depth and beauty—or at times its horror—is an action of love, a revealing of "the bond of unity" which makes our universe a *universe* and not chaos, or a revealing of tragic disruption of unity. Whether the work is a prophetic protest against man's inhumanity to man and the mechanization of the human by the misuse of the machine as in Picasso's *Guernica*, or whether it is a work quietly aflame with the glorious unity and beauty of God's creation, as in Giotto's paintings, the Christian rejoices in artistic knowing as a mode of loving.

We must see what has been happening in Western civilization these last centuries not as the inevitable result of modern empirical science and technology but as the result of man's ancient malady, sin, using new forms of expression. The rise of new scientific modes of knowing and of technical methods of using our knowledge was the occasion of new temptations for Church people and for those who were alienated from the Church (and later from the Churches). Perhaps it is best called the "secularization" of

Western culture. The closing movement of my thought for this panel, therefore, has to do with this secularizing movement.

First, I should like to maintain that Christianity was an indispensable—indeed the indispensable—ingredient in that complex of historical currents out of which modern science—indeed our modern world—alone could come. While all human cultures have developed some degree of empirical science, it is indisputable that the progress of experimental science and technology in the last four or five centuries of Western Civilization is absolutely unique. Nothing like it appeared or promised to appear in any other culture—even that of classical Greece—although some of those cultures are much older than ours—Chinese and Indian cultures, for instance. This unprecedented and unexpected rise and progress of experimental science and technology is usually explained by the secularized mind as due to the Renaissance's recovery of the beginnings which were made by Classical Greece.

The Greek beginnings in experimental science were a necessary basis for modern science. But when Christianity went into the Graeco-Roman world in the person of such missionaries as St. Paul, Graeco-Roman high paganism was blighted by a false dualism which set spirit and matter in ultimate warfare. For that religious culture, man's ultimate foes were inscrutable change and death. These were rooted in materiality and time. Physicality and time were the prison houses of the rational souls of men. Man's redemption lay in his going above time and matter, history and society into the eternal, immaterial perfect realm. However the mode of deliverance was conceived and in whatever categories both man's predicament and his deliverance were described, this world-view is present in Plato, Aristotle, the Stoics, Greek mystery religions, neo-platonism, Manicheanism and Gnosticism. Some felt, it is true, that there was no ultimate deliverance and that union with the eternal expressed in the virtues of justice, temperance, fortitude and good practical judgment (prudence) were all that were possible for man whose concrete existence was terminated by death as were all of his achievements in culture and history. History, as well as individual, personal man, was in bondage to change and decay, to the biological cycle of birth, maturation, senility and death. Democritus, for instance, did not have the optimism of Dr. White.

The collision of Biblical Christianity with this pagan world-view was sharp. It continued for centuries. The Christian world-view itself was wounded and partially—though temporarily—distorted. But the issues were clear. Against every form of paganism, Christianity affirmed the goodness of this world of matter, space, time, society, history. It did this on the basis of three great doctrines. First, the Doctrine of Creation: the One, Living, Personal, Almighty God had created and now sustains all that is and it is good. God created matter, time, human sociality; and history is the sphere in which His purpose is being worked out.

Secondly, the Doctrine of the Incarnation of the Eternal Son of God: God Himself, in the person of His Son, took into unity with Himself a human nature from its inception and forever. The Word of God became flesh and dwelt among us in a particular space, Palestine; in a particular time, the first century; in a particular religious culture and society, Judaism. Space, time, society and history were being redeemed in Him and will be finally redeemed by

Him. They are basically good and need not to be finally escaped from but are to be finally transformed by the transcendent God.

And thirdly, the Doctrine of *The Consummation* of *all* things: Christian redemption is the redemption of the whole Universe, lock, stock and barrel. Materiality expresses Holy Spirituality, time is filled up with eternity, society becomes the Kingdom of God, and history is consummated in an everlasting age which at one and the same time is an age among the historical ages and also the consummation, the perfecting, the fulfillment of all the ages of human history.

It was about twelve hundred years before this Christian world view permeated the whole of Western culture. Graeco-Roman culture died, despite the Church's effort to transform and save it. So the Church took aboard itself the intellectual and cultural goods of that Classical Culture. The Church was like a Noah's Ark, the saving principle of continuity between the dead Greece and Rome and the Modern World.

One has only to look at the thirteenth century to see the beginning of the fruits of the victory. Everywhere the redemption of all things is being expressed not only as a future hope but as an actuality. Franciscanism is not merely a cloistered monastic group apart from and above the world but a missionary friar group penetrating and converting the world. For everything is a good creature of God made by Him and being redeemed by His Incarnate Son. St. Francis was not a sentimentalist when he sang with Brother Sun and Sister Moon and with the winds and the water and even Sister Death, the Death of the body, for Christians fear not the death of the body but only the second death, Damnation. In this thirteenth century, Aristotle—received from Islam through Averroes—replaces Plato as the philosopher most appreciated and used by the great and radical theologians, Albert the Great and St. Thomas Aquinas. In this century, Joachim of Fiore (d. 1202) becomes a great influence. His "The Eternal Gospel" is the first philosophy of history since the early Chialists which expects a new period of history better than his present which is not yet the final age. His book became something like a second Bible for the Franciscans. It is not accidental that the beginnings of Renaissance "Naturalistic" Art appear in Cimabue and Giotto, Giotto who did the frescoes on the walls of the Franciscan Chapel in Assisi. Nor is it an accident that Roger Bacon, a Franciscan friar, was one of the first men, if not the first, to suggest textual criticism of the Bible and to speak of experimental science.

The Renaissance, the Renascence, was not merely the rebirth of Classical Greek culture. Greek culture was reborn, conceived by the Christian Holy Spirit from a Christian womb, the Church. Western man and Western culture were new, unprecedented, unique, impossible except as resultant from the Christianization of culture. The Christian understanding of matter, time, plants, animals, man, society and history was prevailing and the modern world was in the making.

But beginning also was the Second Fall of man. The Inquisition beat Galileo over the head with Aristotle's Astronomy in the name of Christ. The Church in part was obscurantist and suppressive toward the new knowledges. And Renaissance Art and Science expressed the arrogance of Adam by beginning to understand Christian man and Christian culture as natural man and mere human achievement. Deism set in, and a Deist—like a Unitarian—is a man "who in his short life-time has not yet had time to become an atheist" (Louis de Bonald). And then came the tides and fruits of secularism, of which Nazism and Communism were the most visible and powerful—but by no means the exclusive—expressions. As Arnold Toynbee once said the history of the West since the seventeenth century is "The vain repetiton of the Gentiles," the effort of man to exercise his own dominion over God's creation without first accepting God's dominion over man and the Creation. As St. Paul wrote of the Roman world, western men "claiming to be wise (they) became fools and exchanged the glory of the immortal God for images resembling mortal man, or birds or animals or reptiles" (Romans 1:22). We moderns understand that when man deserts or loses God in Christ, he can no longer understand himself in terms of "The Son of Man," i.e. the True Man, our Sonship to God in the very Godhead itself. He may then not only understand himself in terms of what he has in common with the animals, namely the vital powers (sex and race) and become enslaved to them, but he may understand himself in terms of what he has in common with his own creation, the machine, and become "the organization man," "the armed forces," "the hidden persuaders," "the status seekers," "the lonely crowd" of human atoms externally related as are the parts of a machine. One of the deepest questions of our time is, "How long can a disinterested experimental science and a humane use of its results continue in an increasingly secular ethos?" Another way to state this question is to ask, "Does not secularism inevitably break down and give way to demonic religions?" Dr. Yinger has said that the social sciences in any full, disinterested way are not possible in totalitarian societies but find democratic societies necessary for their growth and humane use. How necessary ultimately is the Christian world-view and its practice to the continuance and spread of democratic societies? If the Western democracies fail, can other democratic societies which have arisen on the basis of Western views and examples, continue?

But the powers of secularization in the West are not the only powers by any means. The Christian people have not only survived these last centuries but they have been humbled and purified. The best theologians are not obscurantist or repressive in regard to the sciences and their use. They know that there was never a battle between Christianity and experimental science. The war was between Christians who sanctified antiquated scientific world views with Christianity and scientists who sanctified non-Christian and anti-Christian world views with "irrefutable scientific factuality."

Our present predicament did not arise overnight and it will not be overcome in a day. But the church's struggle for unity continues and the church's mission goes on. The continuing struggle against the enemy secularism may check and even reverse its prevalence, even as the ultimate victory tarrieth long. And whatever may be the immediate outcome of this period of history, or whatever may be future or termination of this planet, there is no doubt about the *final* outcome of God's universe. God is God and there is none beside Him. All power derives from and is sustained by Him. No power, therefore, can prevail against Him and His is the Victory. Only one thing finally matters, therefore: whether we are His. If we have offered ourselves to

God in unity with Our Lord's perfect self-offering, then St. Paul writes to us as he wrote to the Christians in Corinth:

> For all things are yours, whether Paul or Apollos or Cephas or the world or life or death or the present or the future, all are yours; and you are Christ's; and Christ is God's (I Cor. 3:21-23).

# DISCUSSION THREE

Dr. White: I'm delighted, actually, not to have to quarrel with either of the speakers! In fact, my own experience strongly supports what they have said, and I would like to express very briefly some of my own experiences.

Years ago, Richard Cabot, whom some of you may have known or heard of, established a hospital social service at the Massachusetts General Hospital. This had been lacking before, although the family doctor often did his own social service and clinical ministry, too. My father did that, I'm sure, although he called occasionally for help from somebody who could carry out the social service or ministry better than he could. (He was, I might say, the head of the Baptist Deacons in our church. I was then a Baptist, but I can change; I can be a very satisfactory member of a good many churches!)

Well, the hospital social service wasn't enough. It was much better than just a medical service alone, which could not carry out some of the recommendations the doctors themselves made, but it was evident that more was needed. So Richard Cabot established clinical ministry at the Massachusetts General Hospital. The point I wanted to emphasize is that the physical and the mental still need spiritual aid. Especially I would agree that social and medical service is no substitute for religion, and that the physician has an obligation to use social services and clinical ministry, and if wise, recognizes this, and practices calling them in as he needs them, as specialists in these fields. And I would like to add also that the impact of medical research on social science is considerable and important.

One other point I might make is that the problems of medical science may have similar needs to be met as do the problems of social science. For example, the best solution to the perplexities faced by aging people, in my experience —problems including medical needs, and social, economic and psychological needs as well—is to keep our old folks at work. Here is where one therapeutic measure helps them in all these fields, and also, I am sure, in their spiritual needs, too.

DR. MURPHY: It seems to me that the organizers of this panel, either deliberately or by inadvertence, put these several subjects in their proper order. I have thought from the outset that the subject this evening was the crucial one. As we indicated last night, the scientific explosion, the explosion in human knowledge which we call "scientific" (using the term as Americans do) has non-scientific by-products which are the most significant ones. Those by-products—economic, political, social, cultural—are the ones that have the real impact, and create the real problems.

Parenthetically, I have always felt that it is most unfortunate that in the English language we use the word "science" as we do. The Germans use it very much better. They have the word "Wissenschaft". They speak of "Naturwissenschaft" to mean the natural sciences, and "Socialwissenschaft", to mean the social sciences. They even speak of "Humanistiwissenschaft", which are the humanistic sciences, if you must translate. Really, the Germans are using the word "scholarship", "curiosity", "applied curiosity", in every field of human activity. If we could somehow establish this meaning, we will begin to understand that the whole spectrum of human curiosity is valid, whether we are dealing with an atom or with a bacterium, or with a group of people in a structure.

It seems to me that Dr. Yinger put his finger on the central issue, that any religion maintains and keeps its vitality only as long as the society of that time finds it relevant to their needs, serving to give them understanding or patience or capacity to solve their basic problems. And I would like to draw a quick parallel. There is no doubt about the fact that religion was enormously relevant to medieval man. You have only to look at a medieval tapestry or a medieval painting to see this. Let us visualize a set of tapestries done in the upper Rhine in the late medieval periods, say the early fourteenth century. There you will see Christ on the way to Golgotha carrying the cross, and in this set of tapestries, at each of the Stations, you will see the people dressed in the costumes of the times. You will see a contemporary scene woven by the artist or painted by the painter. And the scene is not the barren hills of Jerusalem; it is a scene laid in a village very near to where the artist lived.

Now, obviously, this was not unnatural to the people. It was not sacrilegious in medieval times to put a bit of sacred history into the clothing and the geography of the moment. Can you imagine what would happen today if a painter should paint the Last Supper with the gentlemen in dinner jackets, in the Waldorf or something of that sort? This may sound overstated and I don't mean to sound sacrilegious; but in principle, it was not sacrilegious at a time when these factors in their history had real, personal, human relevance. Now, again, it seems to me that what Dr. Yinger has been saying, and what I have felt all along, is that religion can give ethical direction in this explosive period in our history only as the people feel as intimately related to it as others did in other times.

Finally, I would like to say, in response to Dr. Mollegen's closing comment, that I thought he made an extraordinarily persuasive statement. It seems to me, though, we all fall into the bad habit of closing a set of comments by saying, "somehow it will all come out right in the end." I think we have to believe that; but the point I would like to make is that in order really to let it happen, we have to insist that we all are going to participate in *making* it "come out all right in the end." We look around us and see the kind of social injustices that continue to exist in our society, and most of us happily rationalize, rather than take the difficult bullet and bite it. I would like to leave the note that until that time, in our country, when men are dealt with on the basis of fundamental human dignity and nothing else, until that time, the job for everyone in this room is certainly undone.

MR. WELLS: From time to time in the last three evenings it has been suggested that perhaps there are some limits beyond which scientific research should not go. Tonight Dr. Yinger put a little different light on this. He raised the question, I believe, in connection with the application of scientific knowledge, particularly in the field of the social sciences. He put it rather as a personal challenge, I felt, which I feel somewhat obliged to answer. I think I would answer it by saying that the social scientists with whom I am acquainted, who are working in the industrial field, to the best of my knowledge are all interested primarily in the well-being of the individual rather than in the manipulation of individuals, which was suggested to us tonight as a possible danger in the application of the social sciences.

I might say further that I would not fear the efforts of a skilled professional in any applied field, any more than I would fear the search for scientific knowledge in any research field by competent people, and scientists. I think we might very well raise the question here as to a possible correlary danger. Dr. Yinger used the word "charlatan" this evening. I would pose the question whether perhaps we might not have more to fear from that charlatan who is in a position to manipulate not a few hundred people or a few thousand people, as might be the case in our largest industrial complexes, but one who is in a position to manipulate the thoughts and actions of a few million or many millions of people. Lest I be misunderstood, I am not putting everyone in Madison Avenue in the same category! But I would like to suggest that perhaps here is an area in which we do need skilled professionals. I am sure there are some skilled professionals in this area. But certainly here is an area in which we might very well fear the application of the social scientists or social science, perhaps far more than we might have to fear it in an industrial organization.

DR. YINGER: I was sure Dr. Wells recognized that I was speaking partly with tongue in cheek when I addressed this question to him, trying to make the point that the discovery of knowledge is not necesarily always the discovery of the roads we might take in using that knowledge.

Certainly in the era of the atomic bomb we don't need to be sensitive to the fact that our knowledge has dangerous consequences, and that one of the tasks, I take it, of this whole symposium is to impose strongly upon us the obligation of studying and working with the problem of how to use the knowledge that science is presenting us.

We are under strict orders from Bishop Bayne to insult, at least once, every member of the panel or we don't get our pay. I think I am behind in my quota, and I think I'll go after Dr. Mollegen a little. If I am not mistaken, he made a rather ethnocentric assumption that somehow Christianity is necessary to democracy. I would hope he didn't mean quite what I heard him say. It would be a rather sad thing in the world if we at this stage proclaimed to the rest of the world that democratic institutions are impossible unless you share our particular religious faith. There has been a good deal of careful study of the kinds of conditions under which democratic processes and institutions are possible. Of course this itself is a scientific problem needing and getting careful study; but I suspect that a particular religious faith is not necessarily one of these central items of democratic society. We are at a point, I think, in this highly interactive and close world, where we have to struggle with some exceedingly difficult problems religiously. Let me put it this way. Is it possible to be religiously modest?

Let me also raise some questions about Christianity and science. There can be no doubt that science has prospered more, on a purely statistical basis, in Christian lands than in other lands; and there have been a number of exceedingly competent sociologists who have made studies of this, and certainly support Dr. Mollegen's assertion of the relationship between the growth of science and Christian society. But I think a very important point is left out if one simply makes this assertion. One also has to say that to a very important degree, science was an unintended consequence of certain Christian actions. Originally there wasn't an intention or a plan to develop science. In the first place, the plan in developing schools was to teach the children how to read, so that they could read the Bible in the vernacular so that the Church could be more effective. Among other things, one of the consequences of the work of the Church was to promote science, perhaps even against what it had hoped to do. Now it is one thing to say that science is a product of the intention and work of the Church; it is another thing to say it is a rather accidental, unintended, and perhaps unwanted consequence, even though a result of their own acts.

Now let me be very brief on one other thing, and jibe if I can, not only at Dr. Mollegen, but at two or three others. It surprises me in a group of this kind (and it has happened to me many other times), that non-Unitarian theologians and persons give three cracks at Unitarians for every one at the devil. Being an amateur psychiatrist, this raises very interesting questions in my mind. I won't go into those! But let me suggest at least my own point of view—that it is perfectly possible to be a civilized human being, a Christian, a person deeply interested in religious matters, and not to hold necessarily the views of any particular interpretation of religion and Christianity. I would certainly include the left wing of Christianity as among the stimulating parts of the total range of the endeavor to find out the meaning of the human condition and how we should struggle with it. If I have missed anybody in my insults, I apologize!

THE MODERATOR: Dr. Yinger can draw his pay now. Dr. Mollegen.

DR. MOLLEGEN: Well, I'm going to try to get a bonus! Dr. Yinger obviously hasn't read or at least used C. S. Lewis's *Screwtape Letters*, or he would know the difference between the devil and Unitarianism. To Dr. Murphy let me say that I certainly didn't mean that everything is going to come out all right in history and society. I am very, very deeply concerned about the apathy of the American people —their unawareness of the tremendous crisis that the world faces, and the slowness with which they respond to the only viable foreign policy that they have been challenged with. I do not think they have very long in which to make their decision, either domestically or on the level of foreign policy. And those decisions will have to be continued and sustained, as far as I can see into the historical future. My assurance that the victory is God's, and that the victory is for those who belong to God, is theologically an eschatological assurance, not a Utopian assurance. That's exactly what I meant; and I hope that I yield to no man in trying to challenge the American people on the level of citizenship to their responsibilities of citizenship.

Now, back to Dr. Yinger . . . we have deep and very, very irresolvable differences, I think. I see Christianity as unique in the world; I do not see it as having exclusive possession of the good or the gentlemanly; but I see only two similar religions, Islam and Judaism, as having even belonged to the same type, and I believe that this culture and its institutions are a unique product of having once been Christianized, and I fear for their decay if they remove themselves from this ethos. But this is in no way to say either that experimental science or technology, or democratic political institutions cannot be exportable. Ultimately they must be supported by a view of nature and of time and of history and of society, in a doctrine of man which is like that of the West. I do not believe that ultimately they can survive anywhere in the world apart from such religious support. Remember that the candles of democracy have steadily been snuffed out in the very heart of the Western world. We have had to be mindful that Nazism appeared in the center of Christendom. I cannot lightly say that democratic institutions can survive without Christian support, or that they have a developing future among other peoples without some such religious support. Now in this sense I am much more pessimistic than Dr. Yinger.

*The three "reactors" were called on at this point.*

MR. ADAMS: I think on behalf of the audience that we "reactors" would only thank these people for this fine presentation. I feel that we may have had a lot more agreement than we thought we would find in the social sciences this evening. It may be that our main question would be as to whether social scientists are going to be able to get more precise measurements of some of the great problems that face us—those, for instance, in urban populations in many of the areas where the amount of data is so fearfully inadequate to our finding solutions to these great problems.

MISS BOWLER: This is a comment and not particularly a question. It seemed to me, because I am trained in, and working in, one of the fields of applied social science, that I am very accustomed to the expressions and the ideas that Dr. Yinger presented—perhaps to the point of taking them for granted and assuming that others accepted them equally. I would comment as a Churchwoman, and from my experience also in this respect, that I can certainly see how increased knowledge of the social sciences can sharpen and emphasize and stimulate religious thinking. Therefore, as an outgrowth of both these spheres of interest, I would urge the Church to give more attention and effort to utilizing the knowledge and insight of the social sciences in making religious thought and teaching and expression more relevant to us in the world today.

FR. LANGPAAP: Like the other reactors, I have no specific question. I have, however, a rather strong reaction to the last two evenings which I would like to express in this fashion, and which may in part express yours. I have felt that there has been increasing courtesy between these disciplines—a tendency to want to use and re-employ each other's terminology and vocabulary—a good-humored fraternity of recognition and appreciation. One begins to wonder whether in this evidence there has not now come the time that there is a need for a new vocabulary on everybody's part, and that what were at one time separated disciplines have now reached beyond the point of their separations, and have but a very short time to reunite for the fullness of each and for the benefit of all. The final thing I would say as to my reactions is that either the gentlemen, reverend and otherwise, have been so courteous that they have deliberately avoided stepping on each other's toes, or that it has now come to the time when the cross-eyed bride and the buck-toothed groom ought to get married. And then the big question comes up—who ties the knot?

THE MODERATOR: We have had tonight, from Dr. Yinger, a most extraordinarily broad view of the whole field of social science. Then we heard from Dr. Mollegen a profound statement indeed of the quite arbitrary Christian attitude in the whole area of science in history. We have touched on the fact that there are irreconcilable differences and that it's no earthly good to try to mush those differences up, except for purely social purposes. It was good that they were stated clearly tonight as we have at least by implication, stated them before. The end of this symposium —the end of Christian thought about science—is not to achieve some cheap co-existence. The end of it is to come to the Truth. And the truth is never easy or neat, at least not in this world.

Both Dr. Yinger and I are concerned, as I should hope everyone in this room is concerned, with the careful and accurate and objective and systematic and disciplined study of what people are like and what they do—the way they live and how many there are of them—not because there is any great holiness in these facts in themselves, or some mystery about the quasi-scientific vocabulary, but because it is impossible for us to make the judgments that human beings must make, except on the basis of the best knowledge we have.

Dr. Mollegen brought this point out very fully in the beginning of his remarks—how the purpose of knowledge is to inform and to serve decision; but that it can't do the deciding. There is no way for men and women to huddle up together in some scientific generalities, and escape the responsibility of choice. When it comes to choice, you are all alone. Nobody else can say what you have got to say, and nobody else can do what you have got to do, and no science can help you at that point. This is part of what religion is concerned about—this choice, this persistent and repeated and naked and lonely choice.

Some people would stop there and say this is all that religion is concerned with. No, this is only half of what the Christian religion is concerned with. We are concerned with the choice because all humanity is concerned in the choice. We are part of humanity. But "being" comes before "doing," with Christians. What *is* comes before what ought to be. The Christian gospel is a proclamation of certain things that are so; and these are things that mainly cannot be measured and weighed and tested. These things that are so, that are the basis of the Christian proclamation, are those things that lie beyond science. I quoted Monday night the little tag from Ortega—his question as to whether enough thought had been given to the number of things that have to be kept alive in the human spirit if the spirit of science is to be kept alive. This is the great question. What are the things that lie behind science? Why is it important to tell the truth? What is there that is so sacred about objectivity? What compulsion is there in the universe, what sanction under the stars, that makes a man draw a straight line? These are questions that no scientist can answer solely as a scientist.

No religion can answer these things either, because religion is but a social institution, relevant or irrelevant.

Christianity, as I come to think in my old age, is not really a religion at all. It is a certain proclamation about what is; and it is on the basis of this profound proclamation of God and His continued creation, and His teaching, and His loving which is expressed in His teaching, however painful the teaching is, and His salvation of us—it is on the basis of these facts that we order and bind ourselves. Now I don't know whether this is relevant to our society. I would be quite content to accept the judgment of the social scientists or the medical scientists or any other kind of scientist as to the relevance of the Episcopal church—the religion which is expressed in our church—to our society. I might even know as much as they do about the relevance of the Episcopal Church to our society. Doubtless in the long run we are going to get an answer to that question supplied by many eager enemies and friends! But the question that cannot be measured, either by bishops or by social scientists, is how relevant this society is to Christ. This is quite a different question. And this is really where our whole job begins.

# IV

## WORSHIP, UNITY, STEWARDSHIP: A SERMON

THE RT. REV. STEPHEN F. BAYNE, JR.

# Worship, Unity, and Stewardship

The Rt. Rev. Stephen F. Bayne, Jr.

*Let a man so account of us, as of the ministers of
Christ, and stewards of the mysteries of God*
I. Corinthians 4:1—

I WANT to say three things to you tonight. The first
is about worship. The second is about truth. The third
is about responsible freedom and stewardship.

## I

*First, worship:* Tonight we complete what we have been
doing together for the past three evenings. And we complete it in the most characteristic Christian way, by raising
our whole conversation and all our thoughts to the level of
worship. This is the way Christians act. To us it is never
enough simply to think and talk. It is never enough merely
to know. It is not enough even to act on what we know,
unless that act is an act of worship—unless our act includes
God, unless we are acting toward God as well as among
men in this world.

In worldly eyes, worship is always incidental to something else. When we act as worldlings, we worship in order
to gain some other end—to stir our emotions or to adorn a

worthy purpose or to provide a beautiful setting for some gathering or common act. But to Christian faith, worship is an end in itself. Indeed it is the noblest of all ends. We worship because God exists, not because worship helps something else to happen. If God exists at all, He is the supreme fact, the commanding fact. And our response to Him, in worship, is the supreme act, the commanding act, of all possible human acts.

Therefore it is never enough just to talk, or just to know. It is not even enough to act on our knowledge, unless that act is an act of worship. It is God who creates what we talk about. It is God who teaches us what we know. Everything which has been in our mind this week has come from Him; what we know is true because He makes it so; and we know it because it is His will to teach it to us, and make us capable of knowing it and acting on it. We have talked about scientific knowledge, about the application of nuclear science to medicine, about changes in industrial technology, about the form of new things born out of new knowledge of the universe and of ourselves, and the significance of all these things for our life. But in all this, what we were really talking about was God.

All our learning is only our way of reading His mind, and discovering His thoughts. It could not happen except that He wants it to happen, and makes it possible that it shall happen. Even the very act of learning itself is only the way God's continuing, patient, pressing act of teaching looks, from our side. Therefore it is holy all the way through—the truth as He makes it, the truth as He teaches it, the truth as we learn it, the truth as we do it. It is all holy in itself, and it calls for worship, above all the other responses we make, and in them all.

This is a problem for us. It may be that it is one of the central problems of our world. We have let our thought about God become so separated from our thought about science that it seems almost unnatural—almost wrong—to bring them together as we are in this act of worship. We have slipped into thinking that the world of science is a universal and public world, dealing with the universal things of industry, of politics, of warfare, of laboratories and satellites and weapons and all the other public things. So equally we have come to think that the world of religion is a private world, that has to do with unrealities—with hopes and illusions, with needs and dreams and a kind of extra dimension which is added on to life by those who feel they need it and want it. We have almost said that scientific truth is for everybody, but that God is only for those who believe in Him; that scientific truth is real but God is something not real, at least in the same sense that a scientific observation is real.

Therefore two things have happened to us. Our idea of God has diminished—and this is a problem for all believers. But so has our idea of science diminished. And this is a problem for more than just believers. If our God is too small, this makes both our religion and our science sick and dangerous. Once we lose the sense of the greatness of knowledge, we have lost the only safeguard we have against the misuse of it. Man is not good enough to manage what he knows, unless he understands what its real size is. We will not even keep what we know, much less use it aright, if we do not know what it really is, and what its final dimensions are.

Jesus spoke once about this, when He told about the stupid servant who took the money his master gave him, and did not put it to work but simply wrapped it up to keep it safely. And when the master came back, he said "you knew that I was an austere man, taking up what I had not laid down, and reaping what I did not sow." And then he said about the servant, "even what he hath shall be taken away from him." You may think such a person harsh; but I tell you that this is precisely the way God deals with us. He does not teach us for fun, or so that we will have more power to use for our own purposes. He teaches us so that what He sows may bear a harvest for Him. He takes up what He did not lay down; He reaps what He did not sow. He gives us minds to seek and discover and learn, and gives us the freedom to do these things and to use what we have learned, to put it to work as good stewards; this is the harvest He intends to reap; and if we do not accept His gift on His terms, then we are not permitted to keep it on our terms.

If there is a God, then the whole transaction of human knowledge—the learning of it, the use of it—all this is a theological transaction. If there is a God, He is not something outside the world of scientific knowledge and power, He is not just a chaplain to it, He is not some long dead benefactor who endowed the laboratory. The invitation to learning is an invitation to partnership with the great God, the only God there is, an invitation on God's terms and not ours, to a partnership—indeed to a deep love, for "knowledge" is a Biblical word for the love of husband and wife—which will take all that we have to give, or else will accept nothing. The decisive division in our world is exactly at this point. It is a division between those who understand scientific knowledge as a profound partnership with

God, and those who do not. It is a division on which everything else in this world depends.

Therefore what we do tonight is the most important
thing we can do. We are not simply adding a bit of pag-
eantry to our idea of the twenty-first century. We are en-
gaging in an act of worship, claiming the whole of truth
for what it really is, a revelation and a stewardship of God
the Father, creator of heaven and earth and of all things
visible and invisible. We are saying to the world: "Let a
man so account of us—scientists as well as all the rest of us
—as of the ministers of Christ, and stewards of the mysteries of God". This is not a preacher's phrase. This is a
sober and solemn statement about what knowledge is;
that it is a gift of God and holy, and that it must be received by men as a sacrament, and kneeling.


## II

*But the claim must not stop here, in worship alone.* What
shall we say to those outside, who do not see truth in these
terms? It would be a mistake to think that we Christians
are the only ones who worry about all this. It was not only
Christians who were disturbed at the Supreme Court's decision about the Regent's Prayer in the New York schools,
and what it meant. That was a difficult and painful decision,
and I do not myself see how the Court could have decided
differently. Americans do not like "company religion" or
government religion, and we have constituted ourselves so
it may not be established. But the decision drove one more
nail into the coffin of Western society as we know it; it
slid still another wedge between the world of scientific
truth and the world of faith in God the creator; it doomed

just that many more children to a life in which God has got to be a private theory and science alone a universal fact. I say again I do not defend the antiseptic little prayer which was cast down. It was wrong in the beginning to have government telling children what they should pray. But what is disturbing to so many more than Christians is the fact that once more we have condemned ourselves to a divided world.

It is a cold world, this divided world, in which mystery and wonder has little place. If we must think of science and God separately, then more and more our true sense of wonder is lost. Wonder, reverence, awe, worship—these things belong to God. And when our world is torn in two, our reverence toward God has less and less content to it (because we can't think of anything particular to be reverent about, except a kind of superstitious sense of magic and cheap miracle). And our attitude toward scientific discovery dwindles from true reverence and wonder simply to a kind of helpless bewilderment. More and more we understand less and less about the miracle of truth. Indeed we may not even call it a miracle, because that implies God. Scientific truth becomes simply a frightening puzzle; we are caught more and more in a helpless indebtedness toward knowledge which we cannot ever even understand, much less repay; and more and more our world falls apart, with a powerless God on one side, and a dark enigmatic power on the other which can destroy us and seemingly even destroy God, and which we cannot understand.

Only as we can restore the lost unity between God and truth can superstition on one side and helpless fear on the other be made to yield to a devout, humble reverence and worship which will give us back the serenity of spirit and

the powerful single sense of purpose and direction we have
lost.

But there is much more than this to be said. What matters
is not merely that we shall find again a lost poise under the
stars. What matters is that we shall be able to understand
what we learn, to find a framework of truth big enough to
make sense out of our discoveries. This is the immense ache
at the heart of our generation. Here is where the lost unity
bites so deep—in our suspicion that the whole glittering
enterprise of human knowledge makes no sense whatever.

And here Christians have a special responsibility. For it
is our certain faith that we are stewards of the mysteries
of God—that not only is all truth of God, who is the
teacher as well as the creator, but also that God has given
us a sure measure by which to interpret truth and see its
full size and relevance. Both the Gospel and the creeds
teach us that it is by Christ Jesus that all these things are
to be measured. It is by the Word of God that all things
were made; in Him, in the Word of God, was life and the
light that the darkness could not overcome; and the Word
was made flesh and dwelt among us; and His name is Jesus.

Here Christian faith leaps ahead in one of the immortal
insights of the Gospel. It is by Christ that all we know and
have is judged. It is by His nature that our nature is interpreted; it is by His use of the things of this world that our
use of them is to be judged; it is by the value that He puts
on human life and power that we shall understand these
things. There is nothing bigger than Christ in the world—
nothing which is beyond Him or outside His understanding
and use.

What this means is that all truth hangs together. To the
Christian there is no field of human knowledge which is

not part and parcel of all the rest of knowledge. Because there is one God, and because all things in heaven and earth are the gifts of God's own will and purpose (what the Gospel calls the Word of God), and because that will and purpose is known by us as Jesus of Nazareth, bone of our bone and flesh of our flesh—because all of this is true, there is no truth which is not part of the single, whole revelation and action of God. There is no fundamental division between scientific truth and theological truth. There is no double standard of truth.

If a scientist (Christian or not) must obey an exacting standard of honesty and humility in his search for truth— if he must discipline himself to be taught by the facts as they are—then the Christian preacher or teacher cannot ask for some easier test for himself. Christians may not take refuge behind the supposed authority of a book or a creed or a church; we may not claim an exemption from the same standards of honesty and humility in the presence of life. But it is also true that the scientist must be willing to accept the fact that the world of scientific and technical development is also the world of the Cross and the Altar. There is only one world; neither he nor the Christian can pick and choose what facts he wants to accept; we've got to cope with the Cross as well as with the atom, or else science is no more valid than a witch-doctor's theology.

I don't blame the scientist who fears the Church. Our memories go back a long time in this, and we know how often the Church has been afraid of truth and the enemy of truth. No man in his right mind is ever going to want the day to come again when the Church shall dictate what science may explore and say. But neither do we want the tyranny of a narrow "scientist." If "scientific truth" is going to mean only that part of reality which can be imprisoned in the narrow box of time and space and the repeatable experiment, then there would be as great and as dangerous a threat to human freedom as any threat the Church ever wielded.

There may be many languages, and I would not force the scientist to use the language of the theologian, nor would I condemn the theologian to have to take second place to the scientist. There is enough truth to go round. What is at stake is not some magical, universal language which everybody must obey. There is no hope of this; there never was. What is at stake is the final unity of all human experience. To a man who believes in God there is no escape from this. To the Christian there is no escape from this. He cannot divide truth. He cannot choose a private world of his own. The Christian can't ask to be excused from the implications of nuclear physics or say that that belongs to scientists to worry about. And the scientist cannot say to the Christian, "I have nothing to do with the moral consequences of this." Nor can he say that he will recognize only those things that will fit into his box. A man can't opt out of the only universe there is. Any religion which can't include scientific truth in its creed is bad religion. Any science which has no place for freedom and holiness and the cross and the great dimensions of the human spirit is bad science.

III

*Another way of saying this*—and maybe this is a more important way—is to say that, to the Christian, knowledge is never simply something to be received as the gift of God and treasured as holy; it is also always something to be the servant and tool of love. Knowledge is something to be offered, just as on the Cross Christ took all that was known and valued in life and offered it with Himself in tranquil freedom and costly love back to the eternal Father from whom it came. Christ is the measure of truth, and Christ is the master of it.

Therefore if we Christians abide by what we profess, we cannot accept any sense of the neutrality of knowledge. Life is always something to be chosen, not just something to be learned. Every discovery of God's truth raises at once the question of its use. When the Bible says that all things are made by the word of God, or when we remember Christ's promise of the Holy Spirit which would lead us into all truth, we are saying that knowledge and responsibility go hand in hand. We are saying that there is no knowledge given to men which is not power; and there is no power which does not instantly require responsible decision.

Nobody knows what future generations will call our age, as they look back on it. It may be, as Dr. Pollard suggested, that this twentieth century is the "golden age of science." But I think myself that it may also be called the age of the troubled conscience. We Americans have a bad conscience, a chronically bad conscience. We look around at all the glittering wealth of things which science has given us—all the hardware in our life—and there is not one of us who does not secretly ask himself what it all is worth, in the face of the misery and brokenness of humanity. Telstar was a provocative symbol of this—it was a sort of minor miracle, and an exciting gadget; and yet mixed with all our perfectly legitimate excitement, we could not help asking the moral questions about it. How can it be used? How ought it be used, so that what it makes possible shall be for the peace and unity of the world? And we all moralized at the top of our voices, including myself. . . . and this is characteristic of us.

So do we moralize about everything science gives us, whether it is a satellite or a teaching machine or more wheat than we can eat or nuclear bombs—we do not feel we have earned these things, yet we have them; we cannot help having them; knowledge piles on knowledge and we are almost afraid that there is nothing we will not have; and therefore we search every new thing to see how we can somehow pay for it—justify our having it.

And we are not alone in this. For real moralizing, give me an atheist any day. I don't know whether anybody has ever counted the sermons preached in the Soviet Union by that distinguished Savanarola, Mr. Khrushchev, but I think it would be a staggering total.

This is the age of the troubled conscience, East and West alike. The sheer fact of the incredible richness of science and all it has given us, more and more removed from anything that most of us can do or even understand, more and more poured out without regard to our readiness to have it or use it—all this has piled up an immense indebtedness which can become an immense danger. A bad conscience which does not immediately find a way to forgiveness and amendment of life is an incredibly explosive thing. And when a whole culture has such a troubled spirit, God only can measure the danger.

I do not say that scientific knowledge is a sin. It is rather a gift of God, and an immeasurable good in itself. Nor is it sinful to have it without earning it. Man can't earn anything from God. There is no way for us to justify what we know and have; it is the gift of God, and it comes on His terms and in His time.

Here is part of our bad conscience—people who don't believe in God feel that they *have* to earn what comes to them. And therefore part of Christian witness must be to say to mankind "you *can't* justify what you know, you can't earn it, there is nobody good enough to know what we know or have what we have. It is God's gift; and only on those terms do you know it and have it." Our first duty, in this transaction of scientific knowledge, is to accept with thanks what we did not earn, knowing that we cannot and need not try to buy it from the good and gracious God who has already freely given it.

Only in this humility is there safety from the terrible self-righteousness which grips our world. God save us from any nation or any people who feel that, by the pharisaic righteousness of their lives, they have earned the right to power, or justified their possession of it!

But one thing more needs to be said. The ultimate measure of all this is man himself. There is nothing bigger under God than a human soul. And here our troubled conscience is a sure guide. What is all this worth, in terms of the common decencies of life for the two out of every three human souls who have no such decencies? What is all this worth, in the eternal fight to help our common humanity find its way to what God designed it to be and to have?

I don't deceive myself about any heaven on earth. I know there isn't any and never will be any. All we know is that whenever we have what our brother does not have, and which was a gift to us at the beginning, there is no peace for us until we have shared it. There is nothing bigger, nothing more important, than one child of God. The worth of all we have is only measured in those simple terms. And precisely here is the ache and torment of our troubled conscience. Every day it seems to be harder to find the way to make our science serve our brothers. We feel ourselves trapped by our possessions, imprisoned by them, mastered by what should be our servant. And here again are our consciences stirred and shaken, by our very helplessness to control and use what is in our hands.

Well, let the troubled conscience underline the lesson. The lesson is that there is no power without responsibility. We are the stewards of the mysteries of God; and all that we have talked about this week—the immense scientific and technical power of America for good or ill—all of this is something that absolutely demands to be chosen. Whether it is grain in our barns, or Telstar in the sky, or medicine to heal our sickness or a rocket to the moon—whatever the form our knowledge takes, the inescapable fact is that we are the stewards of the mysteries of God. It is not enough just to know it. It is not enough just to have it. The ultimate test of truth is that it is something to be done.

The prayer for America, in this century or the next, is the prayer of St. Paul, "Let a man so account of us, as of the ministers of Christ, and stewards of the mysteries of God." America does not want to swagger around the world boasting of its strength. This is not our greatness and our obedience. These things that we have are not ours but His. Why He has given us so much of skill and knowledge is not ours to ask. The fact is that He has. The only question before us is whether we will be faithful stewards of it or not.

All these things—all the terrible unity of truth—all the

demands it makes on our responsible freedom—are hidden in the fact that tonight we have come together in an act of worship. We have said publicly, before God and before man, that all things come of God, and of His own have we learned and built all we have. I suppose our worship is also a way of saying that we mean to give Him, in praise and thanksgiving, what He has given us. I pray that it may be so.

I dare say that I will not live to see the twenty-first century. But whether I shall or not, I pray that it may fulfill all the great dreams of skill and power we have of it. But I pray even more that men may account of the people of that time as of the ministers of Christ and stewards of the mysteries of God, that men may not forget that God is the creator and the teacher, that by His word all things were made and learned, that by His Spirit we are led into all truth, that truth is something to be chosen and done, not just something to be hoarded for our own pride and treasure—this is our prayer for the years that are to come.

# SUMMARY

THE RT. REV. STEPHEN F. BAYNE, JR.

BIBLIOGRAPHY

# Summary

### The Rt. Rev. Stephen F. Bayne, Jr.

IT IS ALWAYS a Moderator's privilege to have the last word. Mine will be brief. The addresses and the dialogue speak for themselves, and both the gifts and the weaknesses of the four days are clear enough to see. My only persistent disappointment, I find, as far as the technical details of the program went, was in a lack of engagement, of prolonged and uncomfortable confrontation within an accepted common task. This was unavoidable, given the limitations of the plan. All that was possible was eight hours or so of public conversation, engaged in by a few in the presence of a very large audience, most of whom were on the side of the angels anyway. The result inescapably was a fairly large proportion of set pieces in contrast with too little sense of inter-dependence or inter-relatedness or whatever it should be called.

For example, the tension between the classic humanitarianism expressed by Dr. White and Dr. Mollegen's rigorous theological discipline never got beyond long-range counterfire, never reached the point where each felt involved in what the other was trying to see and say, nor where all of us were caught up in the tension shared by them. Again, Dr. Pollard's thesis, while it was fully understood and deeply felt by the others, never succeeded in casting its proper shadow over all we were saying and doing. It was like an announcement of Doomsday in the middle of a vestry meeting, duly recorded in the minutes but sandwiched in between a discussion of the Sunday school and a question about whether the rector should try another series of sermons on the Second Coming.

What one wished for was hours and hours of debate, in a small group locked in a room and charged with drafting a curriculum for a church college, say, or writing a required text book for the training of preachers. Failing such ideal conditions, it would have been better for the dialogue had we been able to meet for longer hours, without an audience, and in an environment of prayer and study rather than in a theater. But the mission of the symposium was not one which could have been carried out that way; its setting in the midst of the Fair, its purpose, its place in the continuing life of the Church in that community—all these factors established the form it took. And on balance, I must say that I felt the inescapable loss of engagement (if that be the right term to use) was far more than justified by the solid facts that important issues for faith and knowledge alike were frankly discussed in the midst of the Church, and the way pointed out toward what seem to me essential and urgent questions.

What are these issues and questions? Clearly one was the vexing problem of language, as illustrated specifically in the use of the word "supernatural". Introduced at the outset by Dr. Pollard, the word bounced its way from pin to pin all down the dialogue, and in almost every case it was a difficulty. This is partly a problem in semantics. "Supernatural" is a very ambiguous word, in our time, meaning (or suggesting) wildly-different things to a different people.

But the problem is far deeper than one of word-meanings, of course. The root question is whether "supernatural" is anything more than gibberish—whether there is anything above nature, outside of nature, which natural creatures such as ourselves can know or describe or even imagine. The more the scientistic dogma is accepted, that the only valid description of reality is the mathematical one (or at least the space-time-matter description), the less is dialogue possible between the scientific community and the community of faith. And with this loss there comes also an atrophy of our ability even to imagine what the word might refer to. We are becoming a generation as if color-blind or tone-deaf, imprisoned and incredulous.

The sense of the "mystery of existence", as Dr. Mollegen referred to it in a comment on ministry to the sick, is what is in question here. Or again, Dr. Yinger referred to Tillich's description of religion as man's "ultimate concern", and in so doing, left it open whether mortality should be taken simply as an intellectual puzzle, a perplexity, or as the ultimate mystery, the dark curtain which surrounds the stage on which we make our speeches.

Dr. Murphy, at one point, urged a broadening of the use of the word "science" in the interests of re-establishing both dialogue and discovery. I would agree, with great respect; and even more would I agree with what is implied in the suggestion, that there is more than one valid description of reality, and that there are ranges of reality beyond our capacity to describe or define. Indeed these may be the determining realities in human affairs. The word "supernatural" is ambiguous; it may be a poor word; there may be much to be disputed and improvised; but the *issue* is a major one for both knowledge and faith, and it is good that it was suggested, and the nature at least indicated of the question to be asked.

"Relevance" was another word in considerable use. Again it is a somewhat slippery word, albeit popular. I think I didn't disagree particularly with any of the diverse senses in which it was used. That's one problem with "relevance". It's too easy a word. Certainly every Christian would welcome any increase of the relevance Dr. Murphy very powerfully pleaded for, of the Church to the aching problems of intellectual and political and social freedom in our time. Dr. Yinger used the word with a slightly different shade of meaning, when he raised the question once or twice of the relevance of the Church to our society. And so one could continue to illustrate the point.

But two questions need to be asked about "relevance". I touched on one of them at the end of the third evening, when I tried to point out that the most important "relevance" to be explored was that of the Church to Her Lord. It is one thing to make the Church an institution which is relevant to its society, in the sense of using that society's idioms or accomodating itself to that society's values. It is quite another thing to ask whether the Church at any given time is true to Christ. Yet both are "relevances," I suppose. And there is always the further question, which we didn't get to, as to the degree of "relevance" the Gospel ought to have to any human society. In some ways, there is a kind of glorious irrelevance about the Gospel—an obliqueness, even an hostility to the world—which could stand some exploring.

Enough about language. A second persistent theme was that of the role religion and the Church are to play. In turn, this went back to a more fundamental issue and question, as to what the Christian faith is. Again, we touched on this at various times without ever getting down to it (I don't know that we should have, necessarily). The panel included just about every possible attitude here, ranging from "morality tinged with emotion" at one end, to my suggestion, at the other, that Christianity wasn't a religion at all. It would have been pleasing if everybody had fallen down on their faces at that point and cried "how true!"; but they didn't; and it is well that they didn't, for this whole complex of functions is a most complicated and multi-levelled one.

Almost anything that anybody says about religion or the Church is true. Almost any role assigned to them can be justified. The important questions cannot be answered except by far more analysis and comparative study of all these descriptions and roles, and by the deliberate adoption of some as being the root ones. And in this task we are in midstream, in our time. The unity Western man once had is gone—that unity which made it possible to hold together both scientific knowledge and revealed knowledge in one frame of reference—one vocabulary, one standard and speculum of truth, one world-view. Dr. Murphy illustrated this vividly in his analogy, the third evening, of medieval art with its characteristic adaptation of contemporary dress and setting to the biblical subject. Religion was fully and normally part of the whole, single, contemporary world. Therefore such un-selfconsciousness about dress and setting was possible. Clearly we have lost even the possibility of such un-selfconsciousness in our time. The world of "Church," of religion, is likely to be entirely unrelated to the contemporary world. A clergyman in Tudor dress

seems much more normal to us than one in our own clothing. Vestments are really now costumes, in large part, and
liturgical language an historic incantation, and even God
Himself an antique memory or an ideal or a value to be
conserved.

Where and how unity is to be found again is anybody's
guess. And until it is found, the role and function of
religion and the Church will remain unclear. Of course
it is my conviction that the lost unity will only be re-
captured through an activity of the Church, for the unity
and the recovery of it alike are basically theological tasks.
The unity of God is the only possible ground for these
lesser unities. We did not dwell on all this to any extent,
however, so I content myself simply with pointing to the
issue and the question which was implicit in very much
that was said.

Finally, I must comment on one more significant thread
which kept appearing and reappearing in our dialogue.
That was the thread of responsibility. It was, inevitably,
explicit in my sermon. But from the very outset, it was
present. Dr. White's opening comment had to do with
the wise application of knowledge. Mr. Wells, the second
evening, raised the same question acutely in his comment
on Dr. White's paper. Dr. Yinger, referring to the impact
of the biological sciences on religion, raised in an important way the question of the farther social frontiers
for the responsible use of knowledge. Dr. Murphy, once
again, put the issue in a sharp phrase—"knowledge is
beautiful but it ceases to be beautiful when it is put in a
vacuum or in a museum".

Now all this was not simply laboring the obvious. We in
the clergy do that when we moralize in a tiresome way

(which is one of the dictionary definitions of preaching, incidentally). But everyone I have quoted above is a layman and a scientist; and the issue was taken with very great seriousness by them. Behind their comments lay certain fairly clear feelings. One was that it would be dangerous and wrong to permit an a priori censorship of scientific exploration by the Church (and there was a measure of instructive but bitter experience behind this). Another was that knowledge by its nature demands to be used; the question is not why to use it, but how. Another was the fix the world is in and the demands that makes on our responsible trusteeship.

The theological complement to this was not stressed (not that it did not occur to us)—that God is not an irresponsible magician but the most responsible of all teachers, who teaches us as much and as fast as we are ready to learn, but always teaches us in order that we may have more with which to serve and obey and love Him. But stressed or not, this doctrine lay in the background and informed our words.

No area in contemporary life is more perplexing than this one. Whether it be the question of conception control at one extreme or euthanasia at the other, whether it be the just uses of nuclear power or the permissible limits of subliminal suggestion in advertising, there is no escape from the issue of the nature of knowledge itself—good or bad— and of the relentless choices which knowledge brings. No knowledge, scientific, theological or anything else, exists for itself alone. The ultimate point of God's revelation is that by it men may more fully and responsively serve Him and their brother. But how, how, how?

And there are no neat answers. There may be absolutes,

and I believe there are, which establish ultimate barriers and ultimate directions. But our symposium did not deal with those; it simply pointed the way, as we were bound to do as Christians and responsible people, to the issue and the questions which must be asked. There was usefulness in doing only that much, I felt, because it was clearly an indication of the total character of this task. Scientists cannot and do not determine the use of what they discover. The Church—meaning its official voice—cannot and does not. This is a task for the whole of God's people, knowing, sifting, considering, and fearlessly choosing.

That is enough in summary. Those three areas, where great issues are joined and the most profound questions lie, are the ones which abide with me as I think back over the four evenings of our symposium. I must end by pointing out that the agenda is all implicit in these pages. The main thing we set out to do was to think our way toward the questions that must be asked—trying to see what the right questions are (for life is richly provided with questions, and most of them are the wrong ones), and seeking to discern the tests by which the answers must be judged. This may sound like a pretty tentative exercise. But it was astonishing how much witness there was to it, and how thankfully we felt—I did, at any rate—that God was leading us along, step by step. I must express again my gratitude to all those who took part in the symposium, to the diocese which made it possible, and chiefly to the imaginative leadership of the laity, who dreamed of such a thing and carried it through.

# Bibliography

Abbott, Edwin A., *Flatland*. (Barnes and Noble, New York, 1950. Dover Publications, Paperback.)

Cabot, Richard C., and Dicks, Russell L., *The Art of Ministering to the Sick*. (Macmillan, New York, 1938.)

Teilhard de Chardin, Pierre, *Letters from a Traveller*. (Harper & Row, New York, 1962.)

Teilhard de Chardin, Pierre, *The Realm of the Divine*. (Harper & Row, New York, 1960.)

Fuller, Edmund, ed., *The Christian Idea in Education*. (Yale University Press, New Haven, 1957.)

Hagen, Everett E., *On the Theory of Social Change*. (The Dorsey Press, Homewood, Ill., 1962.)

Heim, Karl, *Christian Faith and Natural Science*. (Harper & Row, 1957.)

Hyman, Herbert, *Survey Design and Analysis*. (The Free Press of Glencoe, New York, 1955.)

Kornhauser, William, *The Politics of Mass Society*. (The Free Press of Glencoe, New York, 1959.)

Leighton, Alexander; Clausen, John; and Wilson, Robert, editors, *Explorations in Social Psychiatry*. (Basic Books, New York, 1957.)

Lenski, Gerhard, *The Religious Factor*. (Doubleday and Co., New York, 1961.)

Lerner, Daniel, ed., *The Human Meaning of the Social Sciences*. (Meridian Books, New York, 1959.)

Lerner, Daniel, *The Passing of Traditional Society*. (The Free Press of Glencoe, New York, 1958.)

Lewis, Oscar, *Children of Sanchez.* (Random House, New York, 1961.)

Lincoln, C. Eric, *The Black Muslims in America.* (The Beacon Press, Boston, 1961.)

Lipset, Seymour, *Political Man.* (Doubleday and Co., New York, 1960.)

McClelland, David, *The Achieving Society.* (D. Van Nostrand, Princeton, 1961.)

Mollegen, A. T., *Christianity and Modern Man.* (Bobbs-Merrill, Indianapolis, 1961.)

Mollegen, A. T., and Price, Charles P., *Existentialism: Question and Answer* (Henderson Services, Washington, D. C., 1961.)

Osler, Sir William, *Aequininitas—and other essays.* McGraw-Hill, New York, 1932.)

Pollard, William G., *Chance and Providence.* (Chas. Scribner's Sons, New York, 1958.)

Pollard, William G., *Physicist and Christian.* (Seabury Press, New York, 1960.)

Previté-Orton, C. W., *The Shorter Cambridge Medieval History.* (Cambridge, 1952.)

Saint Francis of Assisi, *The Canticle of the Sun.* (In Matthew Arnold, *Essays in Criticism*, First Series, Macmillan & Co., 1883.)

Schachner, Nathan, *The Medieval Universities.* (Frederick A. Stokes & Co., New York, 1938.)

Sherif, Muzafer, et. al., *Intergroup Conflict and Cooperation.* (University of Oklahoma, Institute of Group Relations, Norman, 1961.)

Taylor, H. O., *The Mediaeval Mind.* (Harvard University Press, Cambridge, 4th ed., 1959.)

Thorndike, Lynn, *The History of Medieval Europe.* (Houghton-Mifflin, 3rd Edition, Boston, 1949.)

Toynbee, Arnold J., *Civilization on Trial—with The World and the West.* (Meridian, New York.)

Walsh, James J., *The Thirteenth Greatest of Centuries.* (Fordham University Press, 12th Edition, New York, 1952.)

White, Lynn, Jr., *Medieval Technology and Social Change*. (Oxford at the Clarendon Press, 1962.)

Whitehead, Alfred N., *Science and the Modern World*. (Macmillan, New York, 1926.)

Windelband, W., *History of Philosophy*. (Macmillan, New York, 1953, rev.)

Yinger, J. Milton, *Religion, Society and the Individual*. (Macmillan, New York, 1957.)

Zetterberg, Hans, *Society Theory and Social Practice*. (The Bedminster Press, Totowa, N. J., 1962.)

Other references which may be sought in libraries or second hand book stores:

Cabot, Richard, *What Men Live By*. 1914.

Drummond, Sir Henry, *Natural Law in the Spiritual World*. New York, 1887.

Sperry, Dean William, "Religion in an Age of Science," *Journal of Religion, Vol. 15*, 1935.

"Our Moral Chaos: Can Science and Religion Together Establish New Moral Universals." *Fortune Magazine*, May 1942.

*De Subitaneis Mortibus*, Lancisi, physician to the Vatican, 1706 and 1707. (In process of being translated into English by Dr. Paul Dudley White and others.)